Renkioi

Brunel's Forgotten Crimean War Hospital

Renkioi

Brunel's Forgotten Crimean War Hospital

Christopher Silver

VALONIA
PRESS

British Library cataloguing in Publication Data

Renkioi Brunel's Forgotten Crimean War Hospital

A catalogue record for this book is available from the British Library

ISBN 978-0-9557105-0-6

Printed and bound in the UK by
Biddles Limited, King's Lynn, Norfolk

First published in the UK in 2007 by

Valonia Press
47 Brittains Lane, Sevenoaks, Kent TN13 2JP

To Nancy Silver

(1924-1997)

Preface

Trojan Gold led me to Renkioi Hospital. In 1996 I visited an exhibition in Moscow displaying the Trojan Gold originally discovered by Heinrich Schliemann. Long lost, this had come to light at the end of the Cold War and now glasnost meant that it was revealed to the world.

In 1993, a truly amazing discovery was made in the basement of the Pushkin Museum in Moscow.[1] The discovery was of packing cases, which, when opened, were found to contain the extraordinary collection of gold objects known as Priam's Treasure or the Trojan Gold, a collection which had not been seen for half a century. The treasures now revealed were the fabulous objects which Schliemann, the millionaire businessman, pioneer archaeologist, and first serious excavator of the true site of Troy, had discovered at Troy in 1873. These, for the most part, he smuggled out of Turkey, to be housed in the Royal museums of Berlin.

During the Second World War, from 1941 onwards, the treasure was concealed in an anti-aircraft tower at the Berlin Zoo, but never despatched to the salt mines where other valuable collections were stored. At the end of the War, the collection disappeared and its whereabouts remained unknown until it made its next appearance in Moscow, rediscovered when documents from the Pushkin Museum were being shredded. These revealed that the collection was being kept in cases in the basement of the Museum.

Then followed intense excitement in the archaeological world as, in 1994, a team of experts established the authenticity of the finds. In 1996 the exhibition opened and visitors flocked from all over the world to see gold diadems, pendants, hair rings, ear rings, bracelets and other ornaments, all of exquisite workmanship, together with more mysterious items such as rock crystal lenses. Ownership is still disputed; Russia, Germany, Turkey, and Greece press their claims. The exhibition aroused not only the classical world but also the commercial, so that tours to Moscow were soon being arranged. The more ambitious combined viewing the exhibition and then flying south over the Ukraine and the Black Sea to Turkey in order to visit the ruins of ancient Troy, close to the Dardanelles.

My wife, a classical scholar, and I joined one of these tours, visiting not only the exhibition in Moscow but also the site of Troy, to complete the story of the Trojan Gold. Might there too, in Turkey, be something of the Crimean War for the British tourist? Perhaps memories of Florence Nightingale or Scutari. Further investigation surprisingly directed me not to Scutari, which is 100 miles (160 km) from Troy, but to a more enticing and convenient objective, an obscure Crimean War hospital, Renkioi Hospital, close to Troy. A little probing soon revealed that Renkioi Hospital existed briefly in 1855-6, during the latter half of the Crimean War. Now the hospital is completely forgotten, save in one respect – it was the work of Brunel.

Before leaving England, I wondered if anything of the hospital was still to be found. On arrival, to my great surprise, our hotel was not merely near but almost at the edge of the hospital site, a land-shelf skirted by the waters of the Dardanelles where now only a single trace of the hospital remains.

Next day, armed with a copy of the original survey made when the hospital was built, in the half light of the early morning before the tourist's day begins, and counting my paces, I paced the land adjoining the hotel. The physical features portrayed on my map, small rivers which proved in October to be rivulets, outcrops of rock, and so forth, were quickly confirmed; I was soon sure that this really was the hospital site.

Despite holiday homes, the landscape can have changed overall but little in the century and a half since Renkioi. Even Valonia oaks, seedlings in the hospital's day, may still be standing, and the past did not seem remote. As I passed a house as dawn began to break, dogs chained to a post outside, strained and barked ferociously. They were certainly more intimidating to me than were the dark shadows of jackals glimpsed by the doctors on their night rounds long ago. Unknown now to local residents, a very large hospital had once been here.

Why should Renkioi hospital have been built here, so far from the fighting then in progress in the Crimea, 500 miles away? And, once built, did the project repay the effort and expense? And why is it all but forgotten? My holiday over, I decided to find out, and in so doing stumbled on a hospital which was all that the Victorians must have wished for, a model hospital whose story I have set against the background of the War being fought so far away.

Christopher Silver
London, July 2007

[1] Antonova I, Tostikov V, Treister M. *The Gold of Troy*. London: Thames and Hudson, 1996

Acknowledgements

I have relied particularly on Trevor Royle's *Crimea* and Llewellyn Woodward's *The Age of Reform* for the history of the period; and, for medical history, on John Shepherd's *The Crimean Doctors* and Lieutenant-General Sir Neil Cantlie's *A History of the Army Medical Department*. I have found John Sweetman's *War and Administration: The Significance of the Crimean War for the British Army* very helpful in clarifying the administrative tangle described in Chapter 4, and Professor J.M.Cook's *The Troad*, equally so in describing the background of Chapter 9.

My warmest thanks go to members of my family, Eleanor Benson, Angela McDonald, Paul and Kim Silver, Susannah Harley, Tabitha and Evelyn Benson, Basil McDonald and Lydia Silver who have made it possible for me to write this book. I thank too, many friends who have helped in widely different ways, and in particular Caroline Read, Robin Lenman for valuable advice about the manuscript, Anita Ballin, and my friends and neighbours, David Shorrock and Allen Withington. Mr Yüksel Ergen of the Iris Hotel, Güzelyali, invited me and my son Paul to return to Renkioi as his guests; he has been kindness itself and immensely helpful on my visits to the hospital site.

Dr Denis Gibbs and Dr Donald Easton have constantly and expertly encouraged me about, respectively, the medical and archaeological aspects of my study. I also thank my sister-in-law, Mary Pym, and Peter Jones, James Morwood, Anthony Bowen, and Philip Howard, friends of my late wife, Nancy Silver, and of me, for their encouragement and expert advice over matters connected with the Classics. I am grateful to Miss Anne Wright, Westminster Cathedral Choir School, for her opinion of the inscription found by William Eassie, and to Jonathan Evans of the Royal London Hospital, and Alex Attewell of the Nightingale Museum for their help. I am also indebted to Mr Timothy Roberts for allowing me to read and quote from the diary of Dr Bransby Roberts and to the late Mrs Anne Nimmo of Edinburgh for showing me photographs taken at Renkioi. The members of the Crimean War Research Society (http://www.crimeanwar.org/) with its excellent journal, *The War Correspondent*, have always been encouraging. I am indebted to the staff of libraries, great and small, and particularly to the staff of the Libraries of the Royal Society of Medicine, the Wellcome Library, the British Library, the National Archives at Kew, the Army Museum Reading Room, University College London Library, the Swiss Cottage Central Library, Camden, Arts and Social Services Library, Bristol University, the Gloucestershire Archives at Gloucester, Dundee Central Library (particularly the Archives Department), the Hunterian Museum, Royal College of Surgeons, London, St. Bride Printing Library and the Army Medical Services Museum, Ashvale.

Some illustrations in this book have previously appeared in the *Journal of Medical Biography, Studia Troica and Vesalius*.

The Papers of Sir John Hall are to be found in the Wellcome Institute Library; Brunel Letter Book is in the Arts and Social Services Library, Bristol University; Dr Parkes' application for the post of Physician is in the Library of University College, London; and a copy of a letter from Florence Nightingale to Sir Harry Verney is in the Library of the Royal Society Medicine.

Contents

List of illustrations

List of tables

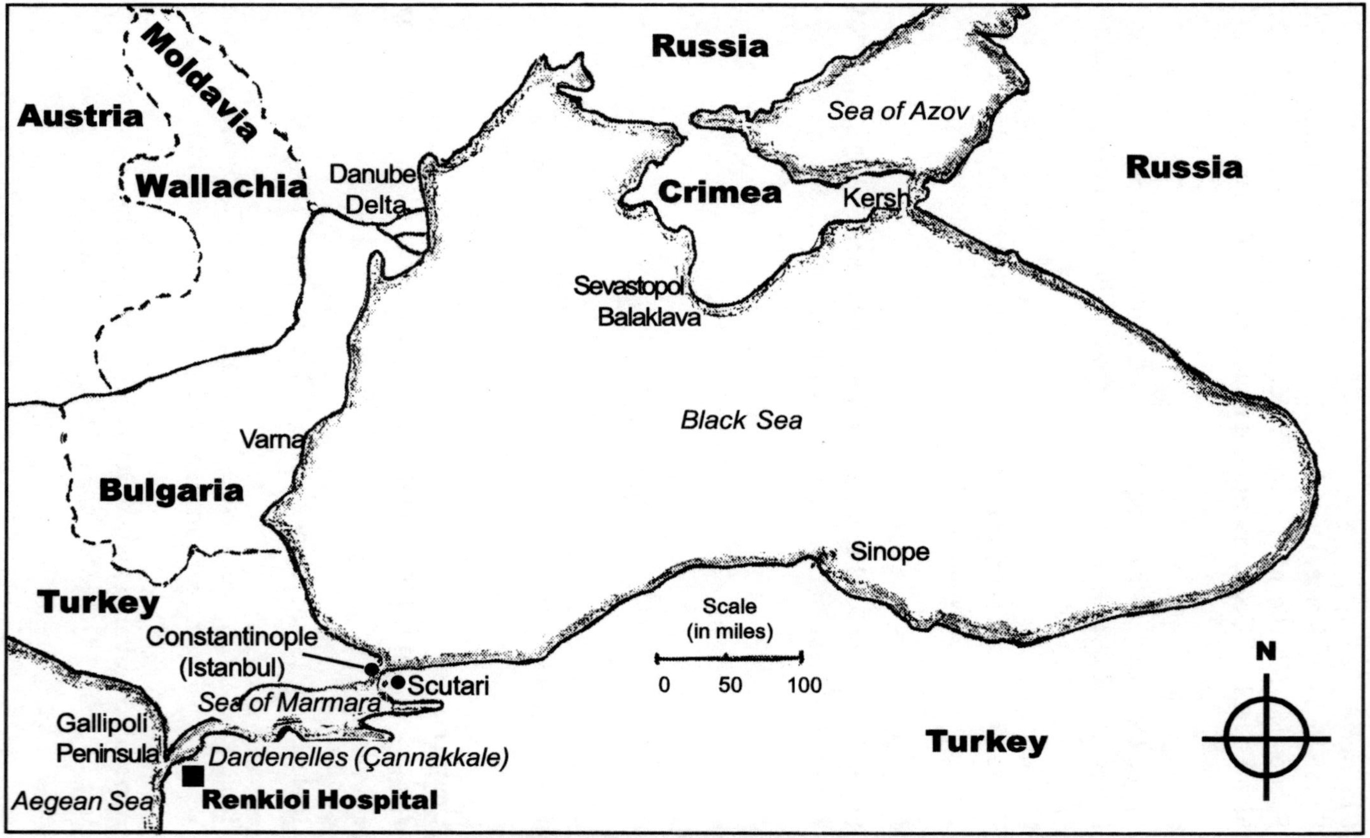

Figure 1. The Black Sea, the Sea of Marmara, and the Dardanelles

Chapter 1

War Against Russia

'The angel of death has been abroad throughout the land, you may almost hear the beating of his wings'.
John Bright, House of Commons, 23 February 1855

The Crimean War is remembered as the first modern European War, in which modern weapons, steel ships, railways, the telegraph, photography, and newspaper correspondents had a place. Amongst these signs of a changing world, Renkioi Civil Hospital should be counted, for it was the first large prefabricated hospital, was conceived as a model hospital, and, unusually, was a civil hospital for the military. Such a complex project was a recognition that the soldier should be valued not only for his courage but because he, like those now employed in the rapidly expanding industries of Britain, possessed valuable skills which could not instantly be replaced.

The 18th century had seen civilian hospitals for the poor founded all over the country. These were paid for by charitable donations, the local landowner a big contributor, and were often known as Infirmaries. Hospitals of this kind became the 'voluntary' hospitals. The rich were treated and nursed at home. Various hospitals, mainly in London, which were to become the most well known, founded their own schools for training doctors. After the Poor Law of 1834, the very poor could enter the workhouse, with sometimes an infirmary for the sick. In the 19th century, specialist hospitals, for children, eye diseases, and other specialties were founded. A few years after the War, the merits and frequent failings of hospitals of all kinds throughout the United Kingdom were described in a thorough review.[1] Histories of individual hospitals describe their governance and rules, the deliberations of the House Committee and various administrative matters, but pay much less attention to daily life going on within them. Contemporary accounts of military hospitals, lit by the extraordinary letters written by Florence Nightingale at Scutari and usually only intended for the eyes of the original recipients, describe the exceptional situation in these. Of Renkioi Hospital, the Medical Superintendent's Report gives an unusually complete account; an account of every aspect of the formation, work, and life of a different kind of hospital, in very different circumstances, emerges. Renkioi was often more akin to a voluntary hospital than to a military one, and in some respects was to be a signpost to the future.

Two personalities dominate the story; they are Isambard Kingdom Brunel (1806-1859), one of Britain's greatest engineers, and Dr Edmund Parkes (1819-1876), the Medical Superintendent. Brunel was at the peak of his career, small in stature but a giant in achievement and was responsible for the meticulous planning and execution of the Hospital's construction, his efficiency a complete contrast to much that was happening elsewhere. Parkes, after success as Professor of Medicine in London at University College Hospital, was at the start of a distinguished career as a world authority on the new science of hygiene which was to be so important to the army.

For the British people, war began on 28 March 1854. By that date Nicholas, Tsar of Russia, had not replied to an ultimatum from the British and French governments demanding that Russia should withdraw troops from the principalities of Wallachia and Moldavia (both Turkish vassal states) which Russia had invaded in 1853, and which immediately adjoined Bulgaria, a part of the Ottoman Empire. Britain and France therefore declared war upon Russia.

The dispute arose from the Russian intention of gaining influence and territory at the expense of the declining empire. That decline was caught in the memorable phrase used by the Tsar some years before when he referred to Turkey as the 'Sick man of Europe'. Russia was suggesting, in due course and in concert with others, assisting Turkey's decline and dividing the spoils later. The immediate point at issue, bringing matters to a head, was the position of Christians within the Ottoman Empire and the access of Christian pilgrims to the Holy Places in Bethlehem, Nazareth, and Jerusalem. Championing them, the Tsar portrayed himself as the protector of the Christian faith.

Turkey, the heart of the once huge, and still very large, Ottoman Empire, could look for support to the British and French governments, traditionally themselves enemies, but by now allies. Neither was prepared to see an increase in Russian influence accompany a decline in Turkish power. For Britain, the overland route through Persia to India and the North-West Provinces would be threatened, while a Russian occupation of Turkey's capital, Constantinople, would give Russia easier naval access to the Mediterranean. All this was the 'Eastern Question'.

While some in the government were irresolute, the public were overwhelmingly in support of war. Not all agreed; 20 years later, asked by his youngest child the meaning of 'Crimea', Bright replied, 'A Crime'.[2] The expectation generally was of a short war and an easy victory, though Russia, after the retreat from Moscow and the defeat of Napoleon, was thought of as the greatest European military power. Turkey was usually conceived by the British public as infidel and corrupt, but Russia was regarded as despotic and reactionary with a military might for which Turkey was no match. Turkey, in the British interest, required support.

The war began slowly, with the passage by sea of an enormous military force, together with some individuals travelling overland through France, to be known as 'the Army in the East', proceeding to the 'seat of war', another commonly used phrase. Gradually the forces were assembled, landing first at Gallipoli and then quickly becoming established at Scutari, immediately across the Bosporus from Constantinople. A base was then set up at Varna in Bulgaria, and the decision made to invade the Crimea. Its capture would secure control of the Black Sea and a foothold on Russian territory. The armies taking part were the British, French, and Turkish on one side, and the Russian on the other. The Turks had been fighting alone since October 1853. Initially the numbers of British and French troops were about equal, but gradually the proportion of British to French troops changed so that by the second winter there were relatively fewer British troops compared to greatly increased French forces. The allied forces were augmented by Sardinian troops, when Sardinia entered the war by a treaty of alliance on 12 March 1855. Small numbers of mercenary troops in the German and Swiss Legions were employed in the British army. At an early stage, the British fleet was engaged in operations in the Baltic.

From Varna, the armies sailed to make an unopposed landing on the Crimea on 14th September 1854. They soon fought the battles of Alma, Balaklava with the charge of the Light Brigade, and Inkerman, but the main operation then became the siege of Sevastopol. Its rapid capture by a coup de main did not take place. The army was not equipped in any way for the prolonged siege which followed, and the dreadful winter of 1854 was spent by the allied armies on the exposed slopes of the Crimea without tents or suitable clothing, and with poor supply arrangements. Though the wounded were fewer, the effects of exposure became obvious and sickness was rife.

March 1855, the end of the first winter of the war, was to be the turning point. Before March, a sizeable foothold had been gained but the best troops were being lost, and, as the campaign progressed, the troops were joined by men of poorer physical quality than the casualties they replaced. After March, as the second year of war began, the siege continued but, with better weather and more supplies, conditions for the ordinary soldier at last improved. Sevastopol was captured in September 1855, fighting died away and the war ended in April 1856. The troops were home before the autumn.

Throughout, only the courage of the army was never questioned, but a shocking administrative ineptitude had been revealed and this was all too apparent in the arrangements for the care of the sick and wounded. Operations in the Crimea started badly with scarcely any transport set aside for medical purposes. Next, the base hospitals at Scutari, seeking only to reach the standards of the Peninsular War, were overwhelmed by a torrent of sick as well as wounded, while the death toll during the voyage across the Black Sea when patients were evacuated from the Crimea to Scutari was very high.[3] To this tale of often avoidable disasters must be added the extraordinary failure to provide transport and even the most ordinary supplies, medical equipment, drugs, food, tents, and adequate clothing and, when available, only to issue them inefficiently with the maximum of red tape, thereby defeating arrangements which were satisfactory.

The base hospitals at Scutari, occupying insanitary Turkish buildings, very soon became grossly overcrowded. Even the enormous Barrack Hospital could not meet the demands made upon it. Florence Nightingale was to call these hospitals *pest houses* and so they were. Their sanitary defects were as follows: 1473 bodies buried close to the General Hospital; stoppage of drains and burst pipes; buildings saturated with filth; no warmth; lack of clean linen; intolerable stenches; infamous sewers; six dead dogs found under the windows of the Barrack Hospital; a dead horse lying for some weeks in an aqueduct; floors of the Barrack Hospital so rotten that the rooms could not be used; and filth and vermin with rats dead and alive everywhere.[4] Rectifying this situation began in March 1855 and took until beyond midsummer.

So the war fell into two parts. The first year saw the invasion of the Crimea, the battles which followed, and then the winter with hardships which have never been forgotten. The second year saw the siege of Sevastopol finishing with its capture and then the gradual cessation of hostilities. In the first year the strain on the army and its medical services, operating within an inefficient system, was enormous. In the second year, fighting became static and only attempts to take the Redan caused many casualties, while organisation and supplies improved. Only the first year is remembered, and the second, when improvement began, is quite forgotten.

As the first winter of the war ended, attempts were made to provide more satisfactory medical services. The experiment of establishing civil hospitals was one. These were not army hospitals but civil hospitals, supported by the War Office yet staffed by civilians. The first hospital of this kind was at Smyrna, but was unsatisfactorily housed and overcrowded.[5] Opening a little later, but by now late in the war, Renkioi British Civil Hospital was intended to be a model hospital, assembled entirely anew from prefabricated parts sent out from England and built on the southern shore of the Dardanelles, 100 miles (160 km.) further from the Crimea than Scutari. Dr Parkes, the Medical Superintendent, when he selected the site, also selected the name, 'Renkioi', taken almost unchanged from that of a nearby village which was then called Erenkioi or Arenkioi[6] but is now known as Intepe.

Figure 2a. Güzelyali. The land shelf on which Renkioi Hospital stood.

Figure 2b. Hospital site. The photograph was taken in 1999 from the vantage point marked on his map by Brunton (Figure 7), shown at the southern part of Güzelyali.

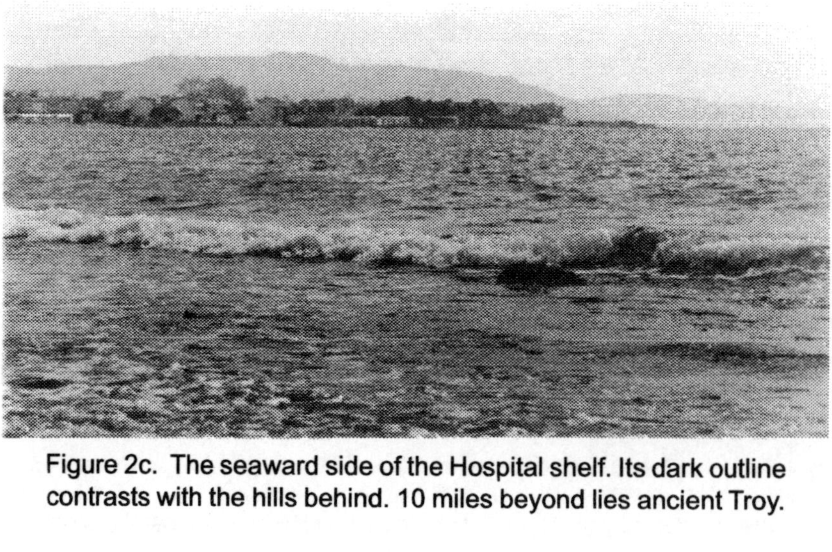

Figure 2c. The seaward side of the Hospital shelf. Its dark outline contrasts with the hills behind. 10 miles beyond lies ancient Troy.

[1] Bristowe JS, Holmes T. in: *6th Report of the Medical Officer to the Privy Council*, 1863. Parliamentary Papers. Report for the Commissioners. Vol xxviii: Appendix 15: 463-743, 1864.
[2] Trevelyan GM. *The Life of John Bright*. 252. London: Constable, 1913.
[3] *A Medical and Surgical History of the British Army which served in Turkey and the Crimea during the war against Russia in the years 1854-55-56.* 2: 465. Presented to both Houses of Parliament London 1858. Henceforth abbreviated to: *Medical and Surgical History...Russia.*
[4] Almost identical descriptions are to be found on page 191 of: Martineau H. *England and her Soldiers*. London: Smith Elder, 1859, and in the answer to question 10007 of the *Report of the Commissioners appointed to inquire into the Regulations affecting the Sanitary Condition of the Army, the Organisation of Military Hospitals and the Treatment of the Sick and Wounded.* HM Stationery Office, 1858. Henceforth: *Royal Commission...Sick and Wounded 1858.* Before this Report was published, Florence Nightingale sent Harriet Martineau confidential information which she used in *England and her Soldiers*. Her book appeared after the publication of the Report.
[5] Shepherd J. *The Crimean Doctors*. 2: 423-427. Liverpool: Liverpool University Press, 1991.
[6] TNA WO 43/99.

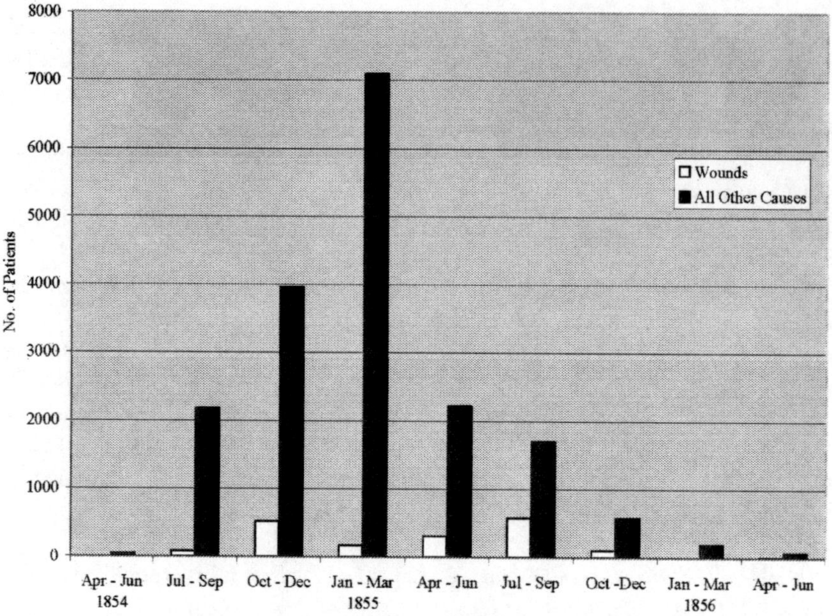

Figure 3: Deaths (excluding Officers) in the whole army from wounds and all other causes, April 1854 - June 1856
Source: Medical and Surgical History... Russia 2: 209. The figures quoted are for NCOs and Other Ranks only.

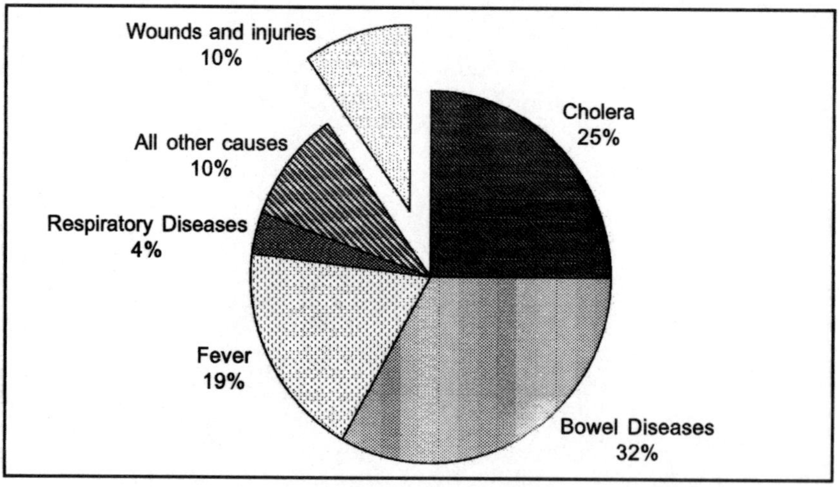

Figure 4: Deaths (18,058) in the whole army (excluding Officers) from wounds and sickness, April 1854 - June 1856
Source: Calculated from Medical and Surgical History... Russia 2: 209[2]. The figures quoted are for NCOs and Other Ranks only.

Chapter 2

The Medical Campaign

> No pest house could have been more fatal than the Camp, the Transport and the Hospital.
>
> *Medical and Surgical History...Russia 1: 257.*

The story of the military campaign gives only an inkling of another enemy besides Russia – Nature – at least as formidable as the Russians. In this second campaign, Renkioi had a part. That part was modest, for the hospital was only open during the second year of the war when the situation was improving. Distinct from an army hospital, save in its purpose, and intended as a model hospital completely up to date and free from bureaucratic shackles, it had enviable advantages over the hospitals at Scutari.

The price of the military campaign can be measured in terms of lives lost. For the medical authorities, those killed in action, either killed outright or dying on the battlefield without receiving significant medical attention, though of enormous military significance, were not a responsibility. Most of those killed in action died in the battles of the autumn of 1854 and during the taking of the Redan that was finally achieved in September 1855. During the whole course of the war, 157 officers and 2598 NCOs and men were killed in action.[1]

Figure 3 summarises deaths of patients which were the concern of the medical authorities. Immediate deaths on the battlefield (KIA, Killed in Action) were not and are excluded. Subsequent deaths from wounds, or deaths from sickness (all other causes), were their concern. Deaths from sickness – Nature's Toll – grossly exceeded those from wounds and killed in action. From April 1854 - June 1856, deaths from all causes (NCOs and Other Ranks) amounted to 18058, of which 1761 were from wounds and 16297 from sickness. Between October 1855 and June 1856, the period when Renkioi Hospital was fully operational, the total number of deaths was 840 of which 109 were due to wounds. Figure 4 expresses the same information as figure 3 in percentages.

The medical services were under greatest strain during the autumn and first winter of the war. As the autumn of 1854 became winter, it was quickly becoming obvious that soon there would be no army left. Losses were due, not to battle casualties, but to disease. Of the sick and wounded, some would die in hospital, some would recover and return to their units, often after a long period, and some would be evacuated to England, often to be invalided out and hence completely lost to the army.

At first, casualties directly due to military action were the most immediate concern. These casualties were those which the public expected. George Macleod, an extremely competent Civil Surgeon, was to give an able and compassionate account of war surgery. This included the passage:

> The injuries which befall the soldier, are, in general, equal in severity to the most appalling of those which come under treatment in civil life. The massive round shot, or ponderous shell, cuts the body in sunder, like the wheel of a railway carriage, or the complicated intricacies of machinery; and thus it is, that as machinery accidents become more common, domestic surgery will become, to a great extent, assimilated to that of the field. The ample space, established routine, careful nursing, and endless appliances of a civil hospital, contrast strongly with the temporary nature, hurried extemporised inventions, and incomplete arrangements which the character of a military establishment in the field almost necessarily entails. The influx too, of patients from the front, or the shifting of the army, makes the removal of the sick in military hospitals to the rear, a matter of necessity, and thus, injuries which might have been recovered from in a stationary hospital, have often to be relieved by amputation; and the treatment of wounds is frequently most grievously interfered with, not merely on account of such removal, but especially as it has to be but too often effected by means ill-adapted for the purpose, jolting ambulance wagons, or ill-ventilated ships.[3]

By the time that Renkioi opened, the siege of Sevastopol had become trench warfare. Although the armament of the Russian army was less up to date than the British, the Russians had cannon of the heaviest calibre and shells more destructive than round shot. Artillery fire was the great danger, though a bullet from the muzzle loaded Minié rifle, recently introduced, could pass through two men in succession and then lodge in a third. The high velocity wedge-like bullet, emerging from a rifled barrel, carried much further and more accurately, and greatly increased the shattering of bone, preventing its reunion and increasing the likelihood of amputation. However, unlike the British, the Russians were not commonly armed with such modern weapons. The seriousness of wounds depended on the nature of the weapons used[4] and the extent of the damage and degree of shock, the amount of bleeding initially or later, and the degree of infection. Occasionally tetanus (Lockjaw), an easily recognized and very serious infection, was observed, and 29 cases were reported during the war.[5] In what part of the body a wound was sustained was often determined by the circumstances of the injury.[66] Gunshot wounds of the head, upper limbs, and chest were most common when standing or advancing, and of the abdomen and lower limbs when lying flat in a trench and taking cover. Injuries varied with the type of warfare; the hand to hand fighting in the battles of the early months of the war became less frequent during trench warfare when Renkioi was open.

Operating as early as possible, and so far as possible removing the ball and all foreign material, was advised, advice which would be given today. The search for a ball might prove extremely difficult, for, entering at the hip, exceptionally it might be found at the opposite knee. Foreign material was usually clothing but could include any debris and stone thrown up by a shell; the Crimea was notably stony.[7] Occasionally, fragments of bone from another wounded man or parts of his equipment were also found and had to be removed.

The problem bedevilling every wound was the near certainty of infection. All compound fractures, with the broken bone in an open wound, were infected and extremely serious, and many led to amputation. Subsequent abscesses were common and needed to be drained. Regular cleansing and simple dressings, no poultices, rest, and attention to the general principles of surgery were advocated. These were pre-Listerian days, and Joseph Lister (1827-1912) had not yet revolutionised surgery by introducing antiseptics to secure the sterility of an operation site; the sterner concept of aseptic surgery, making no use of antiseptics, was to follow. It was realised that when patients were being nursed together in the hospital ward, contamination of one wound by another could take place.[8]

The common major or 'capital' operation was amputation. Amputation made the control of bleeding easier and, with the infected wound disposed of, the relatively uninfected amputation site hopefully would heal. The operation was sometimes performed on the battlefield, with the patient lying on the ground or on some improvised support such as a door, but with less difficulty at the regimental or field hospital. There were many later amputations at the base hospitals usually to deal with infection. The nearer the injury was to the trunk, the more serious the operation. In the period between April 1855 and the end of the war (during most of which Renkioi hospital was open), 779 amputations (non-commissioned officers and men) of all degrees of severity were performed, the great majority in the regimental hospitals. Two hundred and seventeen of these patients died, including all seven who had undergone the most severe amputations through the hip joint.[9]

Shock was well recognised, not the customary emotional reaction to a devastating event, but the sinister grey drawn appearance of so many casualties immediately after wounding or some hours later; its multiple physical causes are only now becoming clear. When present it raised the question of whether the patient's condition would be worsened or improved by anaesthesia, a question then without an answer. Secondary haemorrhage, i.e. bleeding later and not coincident with the injury, was frequent. Again George Macleod gave a vivid and touching account of how severe secondary haemorrhage beset both patient and surgeon, in language little different from that used by Florence Nightingale:

> The haemorrhage recurs over and over again, and the surgeon, though as near as is practicable, arrives only in time to see the bed drenched, and the patient and attendant intensely alarmed. There is at the moment no bleeding, and he vainly hopes there will be no return; and so on goes the game between ebbing life and approaching death, the loss not great at each time, but mighty in its sum, till all assistance is useless.[10]

Anaesthesia, recently discovered, was used increasingly, but an early instruction on the subject which he came to regret was issued by Dr Hall, the most senior medical officer in the Crimea, which concluded with, 'However barbarous it may appear, the smart of the knife is a powerful stimulant, and it is better to hear a man bawl lustily, than to see him sink silently into his grave'.[11] Later, to answer critics, it was said that this was no more than advice 'to be careful'. In 1846, Robert Liston (1794-1847), then Professor of Surgery at University College Hospital, London, had performed the first major operation under ether anaesthesia, the amputation of the leg through the thigh, carried out in 30 seconds. Sir James Y. Simpson (1811-1870) then introduced chloroform as an anaesthetic in Edinburgh in 1847. During the war, anaesthesia was increasingly employed, but not for operations considered minor, particularly after the death of an otherwise healthy soldier following amputation of a finger.[12] The realities of the battlefield in the early days of anaesthesia are brought to life in the story of Private Kenny of the 49th Regiment. 'Amputations at the shoulder joint of the right side, and at the middle third of the femur of the left, were successively performed [on him] within a few minutes of each other, with perfect success, without chloroform, at his own special desire'.[13]

Attention soon turned from battle casualties to sickness, and though casualties due to enemy action were sad reminders of war, disease was a far greater problem. Prevention was scarcely attempted and the soldier's health was ever threatened. Sound principles, which the great Sir John Pringle had laid down after the campaign in Flanders a century earlier, were forgotten or ignored.[14] In due course, William Farr and others, including Florence Nightingale, taking advantage of information never before assembled on this scale, employed statistical methods to demonstrate what had happened and light the path for future action. Fortunately for Britain and her allies, disease was equally serious in the Russian forces.

One almost universal problem, scurvy, due to a diet deficient in vitamin C, arose through failure to make use of naval experience; administrative incompetence compounded the problem. Fruit and vegetables are the principal sources of the vitamin, but at the start of the campaign the soldier's ration consisted of salt beef or pork, biscuit, green coffee and rum; vegetables or fruit he would often have to buy for himself.[15] Scurvy was the inevitable consequence. In hospital the diet was augmented by the distribution of comforts, rarely containing vitamin C.[16] The Admiralty had paid much attention to scurvy during long sea voyages, and the regular issue of lemon juice to the Royal Navy saw a dramatic decline in the incidence of scurvy from 1796 onwards. This was some 40 years after

James Lind had carried out some of the earliest controlled experiments ever performed and found that the juice of citrus fruit was curative in scurvy.[17] A naval medical officer visiting Scutari could claim much greater experience of scurvy and its treatment than his army colleague.[18]

Despite these advances, the cause and treatment of scurvy remained controversial though it was generally considered to be a dietetic disease. Too much salt meat in the ration, not enough fresh meat, or lack of vegetables and fruit, or of a specific constituent of these,[19] were advanced as likely causes. Although evidence was still conflicting, enough was known for scurvy to be prevented and treated. At Varna, in the last ten days of August 1854, a regimental medical officer, typical of others, noted 'among the sick and convalescents a decided tendency to scorbutus, for which I recommended the use of lime juice, and a more liberal employment of vegetables'.[20] This medical officer, Dr Scot, recognised scurvy and knew its appropriate treatment. However these were not universally accepted views.

While only 178 deaths in the whole army were directly attributed to scurvy, the returns conveyed only a faint indication of its role and never the true extent of the disease.[21] Parkes, writing before the war of the army in India, could say, 'a soldier will often have a certain amount of scurvy for a short time for which he never thinks of coming into hospital... The whole amount of the disease, however, is trifling, and the man will generally do his duty and gradually recover without medical aid'.[22] This was mild scurvy, not necessarily considered serious but, in the Crimea, widespread scurvy was a serious matter making soldiers on duty unfit, and delaying recovery of the sick and wounded. The associated listlessness and pallor, known as the 'scorbutic taint', was for ever being referred to. The most common symptoms were those of anaemia, tiredness, and breathlessness, while muscular pains were another feature. Spongy gums and purple blotches on the skin were common signs. The picture was not always identical with that found in seafarers. Perhaps other coincident dietary deficiencies may have been the reason; these too may have been important. So often, those admitted to hospital were suffering from more than one condition, scurvy being one. Sometimes too, scurvy became obvious only after admission to hospital.[23] Diarrhoea is not a feature of scurvy, but diarrhoeal diseases due to poor sanitary conditions were so common that patients often suffered simultaneously from a diarrhoeal disease and scurvy. This was confirmed by the findings of the Pathology

Commission, at work when scurvy and other diseases were becoming less frequent.[24] If severe, with a more serious outlook, the misleading term 'scorbutic dysentery' was used.

Administrative blunders compounded uncertainty so that even when the value of fruit and vegetables and lime juice was recognised, supplements to existing rations did not reach the troops. Only as the war continued was a varied diet, which included fresh meat rather than salted meat, and potatoes and other vegetables, supplied. Lime juice was regularly issued after February 1855.[25] Of the total of 2096 admissions for scurvy to all hospitals in the whole course of the war, only 260 were after July 1855, the period when Renkioi Hospital was open. This decrease could only have been the result of improved diet and lime juice. The figures quoted do not include officers who, with a more varied diet, were less often affected. In the French forces, there was no such faith in diet and lime juice, and scurvy became more common in the latter part of the war.[26] Even after the war, a half-hearted view of the value of fruit juice could still be expressed as follows: 'with regard to the value of lime juice in the treatment of this affection... some difference of opinion is expressed;... but when we recollect the decided influence which it undoubtedly possessed in rendering the food of the soldier easily assimilated... and consider that the diet of the troops was rather defective in kind than in quantity, we are obliged to claim for it greater consideration than it has received'.[27]

Later, original work dating from 1907 culminated in the isolation of Vitamin C and put the cause of scurvy beyond doubt.

More important to the army than scurvy, was a group of diseases now classified as communicable diseases (Appendix 4), whose causes were then quite unknown. Theories abounded. By the Crimean War, the belief sometimes held that different diseases could arise from the same cause manifested differently in different individuals had gone but relics of the humoral explanation of disease, dating from the time of Galen in the third century A.D., were not quite discarded. Justified by long usage and convention, the removal of an excessive humour, undertaken by bleeding or cupping, indicated some regard though no more being paid to these outworn beliefs.[28] There was, too, confusion between predisposing factors and true exciting factors. The former were matters such as the weather or overcrowding, the latter almost entirely unidentified.

It was held that some diseases, pythogenic diseases, could be produced spontaneously by filth, sometimes after fermentation or putrefaction. Such supposedly putrefactive diseases, cholera, dysentery, or diarrhoea being examples, were known as zymotic, a term then implying a fermentative or putrefactive process but later simply meaning infectious, as it does today. Direct contamination of food and water by an unknown agent was beginning to be considered. Also, there was the question of diathesis or constitutional predisposition, by which some diseases could arise spontaneously or under special circumstances, in those with a particular diathesis.

The germ theory, disease due to a living organism, was edging forward. Parasites and fungi, both just visible to the naked eye or with the microscope, were recognised as causes of specific diseases. The mite Sarcoptes Scabei, which is directly responsible for the skin disease scabies or the Itch had been detected in the eighteenth century.[29]. Much smaller organisms could now be detected in the body using the microscope, and Louis Pasteur (1822-1895) recognised single-cell living organisms, bacteria, in 1835, as the cause of a disease of silk worms. Much later, Pasteur described the position exactly: 'Everything is hidden, obscure, and open to discussion when one ignores the cause of some phenomena, but everything is clear when one possesses it.'[30]

In 1847, Ignaz Semmelweiss (1818-1865) in Vienna showed that disease could be transmitted by an invisible agent when he observed that the contagiousness of puerperal fever could be reduced dramatically when students and doctors attending midwifery cases washed their hands with chlorinated lime after being in the post-mortem room. Pasteur, some 20 years after the war, proved that living micro organisms were responsible both for fermentation and disease. Robert Koch in 1878 described the Anthrax bacillus, the specific cause of anthrax, and the discovery of other bacilli followed. This knowledge was to transform the understanding of communicable diseases and make their accurate diagnosis and prevention possible.

Later, Lister realised that Pasteur's discoveries explained the success of his antiseptic practice of surgery. Pasteur and Lister were the two figures who, more than any others, altered the face of medicine and surgery during the nineteenth century. By the beginning of the 20th century, the germ theory was fully accepted.

Neither Semmelweiss nor Parkes lived long enough to see these developments; Parkes was able to give an up-to-date initial view of the situation in his contribution to the Inquiry into the London cholera epidemic of 1849, 'I assume that cholera, like other epidemic and contagious diseases, must result from the action of a specific agent, rather than from any temporary combination of atmospheric influences'.[31]

The doctor in the Crimean War judged what disease was present by noting a characteristic combination of signs and symptoms which allowed a diagnosis to be made, as it still is, from the patient's story and abnormalities discovered by examination. This procedure was often sufficient to differentiate one disease from another, and diagnosis was usually reached without any knowledge of a specific cause. The question however was always, 'what features or combination of them were really specific to a particular disease?'

Often, arriving at a diagnosis could be very difficult. Just before the war, in 1849, William Jenner, the great friend and colleague who was to take Parkes' place while he was away at Renkioi, published the first of his studies proving that Typhus and Typhoid are individual diseases; he republished these in 1893.[32] By meticulously comparing the clinical features (employing excellent illustrations of the rashes), duration, and post-mortem findings of both diseases, he was able to show that two separate diseases existed. He had separated them without knowledge of their causation. For the Crimean doctor, matters were not usually so clear cut. Though typhoid was considered common, firm diagnosis was difficult and so the illness would be termed fever or diarrhoea (in truth a symptom rather than an entity). Only six cases of typhoid were recorded as such.[33] [34]

During the Crimean War, some diagnostic instruments were being used at the bedside. Fever was estimated by the observer's hand, though two 'fever' (clinical) thermometers were sent to the army in 1856.[35] It was nearly 20 years before the clinical thermometer came into everyday usage.[36] The stethoscope had been in use for a quarter of a century. The ophthalmoscope, for examining the deeper structures of the eye, making use of the optical system of the patient's eye, had been invented by William Helmholtz in 1850. In December 1855, one was ordered for the entire army; it arrived on February 16th 1856.[37]

Diagnosis was woefully inexact but, with so little effective treatment available, had much less significance than today. Up to the Second World War, doctors could look back to the Crimean War and recognise doctors then as their brothers-in-arms. In 1945, medical education was not so dissimilar to that advocated by Parkes in 1868.[38] Classical knowledge was still an acknowledged asset, and studying anatomy meant detailed dissection of the corpse. Much more was known in 1945, but the two eras had much in common. In the 60 years since the Second World War, a torrent of advances in every field has weakened the bond.

Though less rewarding than now, a diagnosis was nevertheless very important, offering the satisfaction of naming the patient's condition, hazarding a prognosis and ordering treatment, of which nursing care might be the only worthwhile feature. Diagnosis also opened the way to prevention. Of the many theories then held about the spread of infectious disease, and based on premises now hard to understand, only contagion is still accepted without modification. Contagion, spread of disease from person to person by the physical contact of bodies, is a common occurrence. Fomites (inanimate carriers of infection such as clothing or bedding previously in contact with a patient) extend this method of spread. The theory which then attracted greatest support was miasmatic spread of disease. It was believed that many diseases were attributable to environmental changes, miasmas, unwholesome exhalations of a tainted environment (for example a patient's body) which could then give rise to disease. Miasmas transmitting disease via the atmosphere could contaminate another person or a mattress or the surroundings, even water or the ground.

Miasmas have gone but the spread of certain diseases through the atmosphere is accepted and brought into prominence by fears of bacteriological warfare. It is now known that in limited spaces infection results from the inhalation of infected droplets, coughed up by a sufferer or carrier of disease, or by the inhalation of dust or other infected material. This is a complete vindication of the emphasis then being put on proper ventilation, avoidance of overcrowding, and adequate bed spacing.[39] Over longer distances and open spaces, insect vectors carry diseases such as malaria (Appendix 4).

A wrong theory often explained one aspect of a situation but not the whole. At least the miasmatic theory suggested that a favourable physical environment could contribute to health. Lacking knowledge of the true causes of communicable disease, the link between poor sanitation and ill health was not proved. Insanitary conditions were regarded as unpleasant but not necessarily clearly detrimental to health.[40] The smell of the poverty stricken home or hospital ward was simply accepted.

In 1855, John Snow (1813-1858) completed the second edition of his book on the communication of cholera.[41] The book now seems an almost incontrovertible argument in favour of cholera being primarily a waterborne disease. At the time, this view was only beginning to gain acceptance and it is interesting to see how Parkes' views about the matter changed over the years. In 1848, he considered that the patient's blood became contaminated by a poison introduced by the lungs i.e. miasmatic spread.[42] In 1855, he appeared unconvinced and concluded a very fair review of Snow's book by saying that it was 'an hypothesis worthy of enquiry', concluding his review by recommending this.[43] In 1864, he accepted that cholera was waterborne.[44] Snow considered that diarrhoeal diseases, diarrhoea, dysentery, and typhoid (classified as a fever but also a diarrhoeal disease) were also waterborne though he did not set out specifically to prove this. These diseases were responsible for most of the army's sickness, an immense condemnation of army sanitation.[45]

The main illnesses of the war were classified as diarrhoeal diseases, cholera and fever. The figures for these were huge, a total of 94,429 hospital admissions and 13,013 deaths (NCOs and Other Ranks only). Diseases with diarrhoea as a principal symptom were categorized as diarrhoea (from unknown but many causes), dysentery (with blood and slime in the stools), and cholera, the diarrhoeal disease most feared which was so distinctive and profoundly serious as to merit separate classification. These figures refer to the whole army. In the official 'Medical and Surgical History of the War', 'Diarrhoeal Diseases' and 'Diseases of the Stomach and Bowels' were interchangeable terms. There were 55,665 admissions and 5,043 deaths due to diarrhoeal diseases, 7,574 admissions and 4,524 deaths due to cholera, and 31,190 admissions and 3,446 deaths due to fever.

These figures are depicted in greater detail in Figure 5 overleaf.

Palmerston could write to his Secretary of State for War, 'Our Quartermaster-Generals never bestow a thought about the healthiness of situations, and indeed they in general are wholly ignorant of the sanitary principles upon which any given situation should be chosen or avoided'.[46] Ignorance and indifference were almost universal, and sanitary conditions were often disgraceful.

Epidemics of cholera occurred in the opposing armies, and though cholera was rather less frequent than the other diarrhoeal diseases, because of high mortality, it overshadowed all else. Characterised by intense watery diarrhoea with enormous fluid loss, in fatal cases the illness is often frighteningly short, of only a few hours duration, with collapse and all the signs of fluid lack, accompanied by great anxiety. The terror inspired, and the rapidity with which it progressed, are captured in the story of a hospital orderly who, told that he had slept under the blanket of a man lately dead from cholera, cried, 'I am done for'; soon he too was dead.[47] It seems likely that atypical mild cases during outbreaks contributed substantially to the number of patients considered to be simply suffering from 'diarrhoea'.

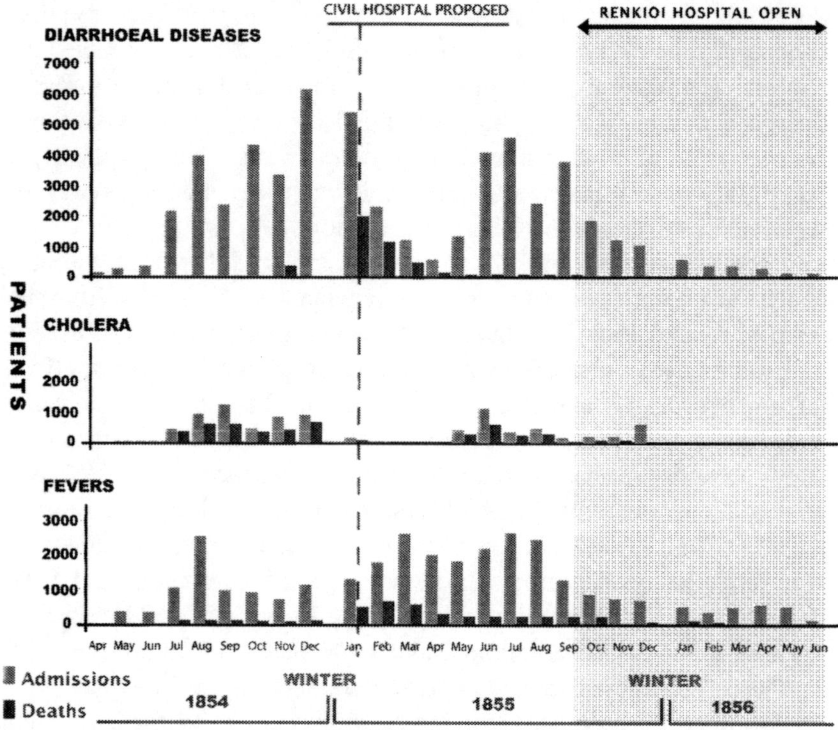

Figure 5: Admissions and Deaths (excluding Officers) in the whole army due to Diarrhoeal Diseases, Cholera and Fevers (April 1854 - June 1856). Source: *Medical and Surgical History... Russia* 2: 127,88,169. The figures quoted are for NCOs and Other Ranks only.

That this is likely is confirmed by detailed studies of modern outbreaks. It can be conjectured that Lord Raglan was such a patient. He died, aged 67, in June 1855 after an illness of two or three days duration with diarrhoea as an initial symptom. His death was ascribed contemporaneously to a 'broken heart'. Death rates of recognised cases were very high, 50% or more. For the Victorians there was always the menace of cholera which, in London as the war began, had made 25,000 people ill, of whom half died. Andrew Smith, the Director General of the Army Medical Department, was to say that had not cholera assailed the army, his plans would have met the situation.[48] 'Diarrhoea appeared as a *mere symptom*, dysentery followed and cholera trode (sic) on the heels of all'.[49] There were well-founded suspicions that the disease could be waterborne, during the war, but it was generally considered to be miasmatic in origin.[50]

Fevers included typhoid, typhus, and malaria with characteristic features. These were now beginning to be accurately distinguished at the bedside from others simply termed Intermittent, Remittent (Crimean), Simple, Continued, and Relapsing. An accurate diagnosis of these illnesses (requiring as yet unknown laboratory investigations) was impossible. Fevers must have included examples of typhoid, typhus, together classed as typhous diseases (the Greek derivation of the words referring to the muddled state of mind seen in both diseases), and malaria, recognised by the periodicity of the feverish paroxysms and an enlarging spleen, felt through the abdominal wall. Though not known to be conveyed by mosquitoes,[51] it was known to be associated with damp countryside. Other fevers are likely to have been sandfly fever, dengue, and relapsing fever, now the name of a specific louse-borne disease. Another, Malta Fever, now termed brucellosis, is likely to have been contracted by troops drinking infected goat milk if their ship, on the voyage from England, made a stop in Malta, or if they were sent to the island for convalescence. This was unknown at the time. It is now known also to occur in Russia and Turkey. Florence Nightingale's prolonged ill-health later in life, which dated from an attack of Crimean Fever, has, in recent times, been convincingly ascribed to this disease.[52]

Important infections included those affecting the lungs, such as bronchitis and pneumonia, and phthisis (pulmonary tuberculosis), which was recognised as being associated with overcrowded living conditions, the barrack room a prime example. Phthisis was the most important chronic disease among troops stationed at home.

Because of the danger of infection, men did not want to come forward as medical orderlies. In one regiment between November and March, 11 medical orderlies died. [53]

The last major health hazard was to be winter. Even before this, however, as they stepped ashore at Calamita bay on the Crimea, the soldiers were without knapsacks, bedding, and tentage. Many were plagued by diarrhoea. Carrying 60 lbs of equipment, they were wearing heavy and uncomfortable clothing ill-adapted to a Crimean September. Over the first few days, rations were scarce and there was little water. Heat must have caused many collapses. The medical officers were without their instruments and drugs. Ambulances had been embarked only to be taken ashore again before sailing. Large hospital marquees were landed at the bay, then taken aboard again and removed.[54] Confusion reigned. These initial deficiencies were not quickly made up.

Soon it was winter. November and December 1855 saw the largest number of admissions to hospital and, January 1856, the largest number of deaths. Although the winters during the war were not unusually severe, trench warfare during the first winter was conducted in appalling conditions. Men were not only cold, but their clothes were drenched and could not be dried. Almost starved, they lay still in the trenches for hours or stood in water. There were 2398 casualties during the war due to frostbite, of which 1924 were in the first year, ending in March 1855, and 474 in the second. The term 'frostbite' covered many conditions due to exposure, some acquired when the temperature was above freezing. Gangrene often supervened. Meteorological records made at the Castle Hospital Balaklava, 275 feet above sea level, still exist for the period April 1855 to June 1856. On December 19th 1855, the maximum temperature was 9^0 F., and the lowest 2.5^0F. i.e. many degrees of frost with, as well, a strong breeze from the north. For most of the period from December 1855 to March 1856, the mean temperature was little above freezing.[55] Summer, not winter, clothing, lack of tents and bedding, soldiers individually responsible for cooking their own meals, and short supplies were guarantees of hardship. Notorious lack of transport made matters even worse. In November 1854, an exceptional gale swept away shipping and supplies. Hardship bore most upon the NCOs and men. An officer could send his servant several miles to secure a chicken at Balaklava and was likely to possess a tent, so, not surprisingly, officers had less sickness than their men.[56] The second winter was very different from the first, for though the weather was much the same, fighting lessened and the men were much better equipped; casualty and sickness rates were low.

In this battle against Nature, the lessons of so many previous wars had to be learned again. Health and hygiene had been pushed aside with deplorable results. Diarrhoeal diseases were associated with defective sanitation; scurvy with dietary defects; and winter's hazards with failure to provide suitable shelter and clothing. All were shortcomings, only in part due to ignorance, which should never have arisen. The medical authorities were commonly ignored,[57] and the failure was not the failure of the medical services alone, but of the army as a whole. It arose from the circumstances of war and archaic organisation and administration; had the enormity of these mistakes been grasped earlier, success might have come sooner.

As the first winter of the war closed, and the second year began, Parliament took the first steps towards improving health in the army. Three Commissions, all affecting health were established. First was the Sanitary Commission which made sanitation a subject for which the military was as responsible as the doctors.[58] Next was the Supplies Commission,[59] concerned with the recurring military administrative failings of the campaign, and last, the Pathology Commission, of a more technical nature.[60] Florence Nightingale, too, continued her great work and launched the career of nursing.

A picture, a snapshot, emerges of the reality of which Renkioi, though distant from military operations, was a part. The invasion of the Crimea and the privations which followed were a menacing preamble to Renkioi's existence. Had it opened in the winter of 1854-5, its value would have been immense. Instead, Renkioi was much less significant. But it was a remarkable experiment, a model hospital, for such it proved to be, beckoning into the future.

[1] *Medical and Surgical History...Russia* 2: 387.

[2] Percentages are calculated. Florence Nightingale and William Farr made use of charts to demonstrate statistical findings. Figure 4 is an 'exploded' pie chart, not dissimilar to the diagrams Farr provided after the war for the *Report of the Sanitary Commission.* These diagrams, with segments of appropriate area representing the number of patients in different categories, made statistics clear to an audience unused to interpreting figures. Farr's diagrams had an irregular outline rather than the circular outline which is now usual so that Florence Nightingale referred to them as coxcomb diagrams.

[3] Macleod GHB. *Notes on the surgery of the war.* Edinburgh Med J 1856; 1:985. This article was one of a series which Macleod later expanded into a book, *Notes on the Surgery of the War in the Crimea.* London: Churchill, 1858. George Macleod((1828-1892) became Regius Professor of Surgery, Glasgow, in 1869 and was knighted in 1887.

[4] *Medical and Surgical History...Russia.* 2: 262-264.

[5] *Medical and Surgical History...Russia.* 2: 279.

[6] Wounds sustained during the capture of the Redan, a military operation from which Renkioi received casualties, classified by the weapons and missiles responsible and the site of injury:

MusketBall	1003
Grape, Round Shot & Shell	654
Sword /Bayonet	253
Total wounds treated	1910

Wounds, Head, Chest and Upper Half of the Body	806
Wounds, Abdomen & Lower Half of the Body	1104

[7] Wolseley Field Marshal Lord. *The Story of a Soldier's Life.* 1:186. London. Constable, 1903. Garnet Wolseley, the future Field Marshal but then a subaltern, was wounded in the neck just before the September attack on the Redan. He felt something sticking in his jaw and insisted on further examination which ended in one doctor holding his head between his knees, whilst the other with a forceps pulled out a large piece of jagged rock. Thirty-four years later he wished to see the Army Medical School abolished, and ridiculed the efforts of Sanitary Officers (Cantlie N. *History of the Army Medical Department.* 2:286. Edinburgh: Churchill Livingstone, 1974).

[8] Goldie SM. Ed. Florence Nightingale. *Letters from the Crimea.* 39, (Letter, 25.11.54, Florence Nightingale to Sidney Herbert). Manchester: Mandolin, 1997.

[9] *Medical and Surgical History...Russia* 2:368.

[10] Macleod GHB. *Notes on the surgery of war.* Edinburgh Medical Journal 1856, 1:996.

[11] Cantlie N. *History of the Army Medical Department* 2:40. Edinburgh: Churchill Livingstone, 1974.

[12] *Medical and Surgical History...Russia* 2:268.

[13] *Medical and Surgical History...Russia* 2:266.

[14] Pringle J. *Observations on the Diseases of the Army in Camp and Garrison.* London: Millas Wilson Payne, 1752.

[15] *Medical and Surgical History...Russia* 2:177. The incidence of scurvy was lower in the cavalry than in the infantry, because the cavalry were encamped near the little port of Balaklava and its supplies and shops.

[16] *Medical and Surgical History...Russia* 2:526-529. Huge quantities (arrowroot, dried vegetables, preserved meats, wine and other alcoholic drinks, cocoa and milk, etc.) were sent out to hospitals from England. None were sources of Vitamin C.

[17] Carpenter KJ. *The History of Scurvy and Vitamin C.* 52. Cambridge: Cambridge University Press, 1986.

[18] Davidson J. *The surgical practice in a Naval Hospital.* Glasgow Medical Journal 1855; 2:475-477.

[19] Attention was now focussed on the chemical constituents of diet such as mineral salts. As Carpenter pointed out (*History of scurvy and Vitamin C* 108, 130), Parkes in 1848 wrote an unsigned review in which he firmly rejected the 'mineral' theories and suggested that the relatively high potassium content of the anti-scorbutic vegetables was only a coincidence. Later he considered the idea that scurvy was due to acidity of the blood arising from an imbalance of acids and alkalies in the body.

[20] *Medical and Surgical History...Russia* 2:171.

[21] *Medical and Surgical History...Russia* 2:171.

[22] Parkes EA. *Remarks on the dysentery and hepatitis of India*. 122. London: Longman Brown Green & Longman, 1846.

[23] *Medical and Surgical History...Russia* 2:183. Mercury, prescribed as calomel, to clear out the bowel of patients with diarrhoea, invariably brought out the signs of scurvy if present, one more reminder of how often treatment must have had serious, indeed sometimes fatal, consequences.

[24] *Report on the Pathology of the Diseases of the Army in the East* 58-84: London. HM Stationery Office, 1856. The Report frowned on the term 'scorbutic dysentery'.

[25] Shepherd J. *The Crimean Doctors* 1.244 Liverpool: Liverpool University Press, 1991 quoting *MSH...Russia* 2:182.

[26] Carpenter KJ. *The History of Scurvy and Vitamin C*. 114. Cambridge: Cambridge University Press, 1986.

[27] *Medical and Surgical History...Russia* 2:183.

[28] The humours were the four chief fluids of the body, blood, phlegm, choler (i.e. ordinary bile) and melancholy (an excess of black bile or the mental state supposed to arise therefrom) and were in balance in health and out of balance in sickness.

[29] Sir John Pringle noted that the itch or scabies was due an animalcule, a term covering a variety of living organisms, their common property being their minuteness. (Pringle J. *Observations in Camp and Garrison*. London: Millas, Wilson, Payne, 1752).

[30] Carter KC. *The Rise of Causal Concepts of Disease*. 119 (quoting Pasteur 1922-39 Vol. 6 pp 110, 114). Aldershot: Ashgate, 2003.

[31] An Inquiry into the bearing of the earliest cases of cholera, which occurred in London during the present epidemic on the strict theory of contagion. *British and Foreign Medico-Chirurgical Review 1849*; 4: 251-276. The 'strict contagion theory' envisaged a specific agent of disease which spread disease by multiplying within the body so that others became infected through contact. The 'modified theory' envisaged the agent multiplying in the body or outside it and widely spreading disease. Regarding the former segregation and quarantine were the preventive measures of choice; the latter could be affected by environmental conditions so that these too were thought important in prevention.

[32] Jenner W. *Lectures and Essays on fevers and diphtheria*. 1849-1879. London: Rivington Percival, 1893.

[33] Cantlie N. *History of the Army Medical Department.* 2: 188. Edinburgh: Churchill Livingstone, 1974. A few years later, some 27,000 deaths were ascribed to typhoid in the American Civil War (Cox FEG, Ed. *Wellcome Trust History of Tropical Diseases.* 32. London: The Wellcome Trust, 1996).
[34] *Report on the Pathology of the Diseases of the Army in the East.* 58-84: London: HM Stationery Office, 1856. Evidence of typhoid was found in many autopsies, 39 of which were recorded in detail.
[35] *Medical and Surgical History...Russia.* 1 Appendix XI, p 560. William Aitken, himself a pioneer in the use of clinical thermometers, contributed a chapter about dengue to Sir John Reynold's *System of Medicine* (1866), mentioning that the patient's temperature in that disease had not yet been recorded by a thermometer. Parkes was using the thermometer for examining his ward patients before the war.
[36] Allbutt TC. *Medical Thermometry.* British and Foreign Medico-Chirurgical Review, 1870; 45: 429-441, 46: 144-156.
[37] *Medical and Surgical History...Russia* 1.560.
[38] Parkes EA. *A Scheme of Medical Tuition.* Lancet 1868; 1: 441-443.
[39] This was Florence Nightingale's view soon to appear in *Notes on Hospitals*, (see Chapter 6).
[40] Mr. Atkinson, a surgeon, in praising the value of sulphuretted hydrogen in the treatment of cholera, commented that not a single case had occurred at Worthing, a dispensation due to the disagreeable smell from eight sewage pipes which ran out to sea (Atkinson JC. *Analyses of communications on the treatment of cholera.* Lancet 1849; 2: 316). A few years later a typhoid outbreak at Worthing was considered to have spread via the sewers.
[41] Snow J. *On the Mode of Communication of Cholera.* London. John Churchill, 1855.
[42] Review. *Researches into the Pathology and Treatment of the Asiatic and Algide Cholera.* British and Foreign Medico-Chirurgical Review 1848, 1:241.
[43] Parkes EA. *Review xiii.* British and Foreign Medico-Chirurgical Review 1855, 15:449-463.
[44] Parkes EA. *A Manual of Practical Hygiene.* 18. London. John Churchill. 1864.
[45] Snow J. *On the chief cause of the recent sickness and mortality in the Crimea. Medical Times and Gazette 1855*, 10:457-458.
[46] Douglas G, Dalhousie G. (Eds.). *The Panmure Papers* 1.231. London: Hodder & Stoughton, 1908.
[47] *Medical and Surgical History...Russia* 1: 368, 2.60
[48] *Medical and Surgical History...Russia* 1: Preface iii
[49] *Medical and Surgical History...Russia* 2: 117.
[50] Aitken W. *Handbook of the Science and Practice of Medicine.* 233. London: Griffin, 1858.
[51] Humphrey Sandwith, a British doctor working in Turkey at the time of the Crimean war devoted a quarter of his article, *A Brief Sketch of the Diseases of*

Northern Turkey (Association Medical Journal 1854: 433-436), to malaria which was prevalent round the Black Sea. The banks of the Danube were fatal to British sailors who were brought dying to Constantinople with quotidian and tertian malaria. Their bodies were covered with ulcers from the bites of mosquitoes. The link between mosquitoes and malaria was established 40 years later. Parkes himself from enquiries among villagers living on the damp plains of Troy believed that the infection could be waterborne (Parkes EA. *A Manual of Practical Hygiene*. 42. 4th edition. London. Churchill. 1873).

[52] Young DAB. *Florence Nightingale's Fever. British Medical Journal* 1995; 311: 1697-1700.

[53] *Medical and Surgical History...Russia* 2: 141.

[54] Shepherd J *The Crimean Doctors* 1: 119. Liverpool: Liverpool University Press, 1991.

[55] *Medical and Surgical History...Russia* 2: 399-464 Summer temperatures reached 89°F.

[56] *Medical and Surgical History...Russia* 2: 223-224.

[57] Sir John Hall summed the matter up when answering Question 5341, Royal Commission.....Sick and Wounded 1858 '...military men do not often attend to the recommendations of medical officers'. In a circular to his medical officers in December 1855, Hall said that he would be glad 'to know if you have found commanding officers as willing to listen to, and anxious to carry out the suggestions of medical officers as Sir William Codrington seems to think they are' (Lancet 1856. 1:101). There is ample evidence that they were not.

[58] *The Proceedings of the Sanitary Commission dispatched to the seat of War in the East 1855-56.* Presented to both Houses of Parliament. London, 1857.

[59] *Report of the Commission of Inquiry into the Supplies of the British Army in the Crimea.* June 1855.

[60] *Report on the Pathology of the Diseases of the Army in the East.* London: HM Stationery Office, 1856.

Chapter 3

Turning the Situation Round

'The army medical staff is exhausted.'
Sidney Herbert to Dr Andrew Smith 19 January 1855

The passage of the army to the East, and its landing on the Crimea, had been successfully accomplished, but soon there were enormous numbers of sick and wounded requiring treatment. Long lines of communication meant that their transport by land and by sea had to be efficient, and evacuation from the regimental hospitals to the base hospitals at Scutari, or even England, possible. Effective measures to meet such difficulties should have been long prepared, but they were not. The expeditionary force which invaded the Crimea had much the same organisation and administration as that of the Peninsular campaign. Fighting skills had been maintained in colonial wars but this experience counted for much less in an entirely different type of warfare. Only old soldiers had had experience of a European war, and the many reforms proposed over the years to permit the prosecution of a modern war had never been acted upon, mainly for reasons of economy. A deadening of initiative and doubts about promotion were the hallmarks of the period.

The control of the army was in the hands of Parliament, and the responsibility for military matters devolved to the Secretary of State for War and the Colonies, and to the Secretary at War. The conduct of the war lay in the hands of the Secretary for War, while the Secretary at War, with the Treasury, had control of finance. His decisions had to be approved by the Secretary for War.[1] The need for financial prudence and accountability was ever present, and meant the checking by more than one authority of both action and expenditure. At the beginning of the war, the Secretary of State for War (and for the Colonies) was the Duke of

Newcastle, and the Secretary at War, Sidney Herbert. Both were members of the Cabinet. In peacetime, the Duke had been mainly concerned with the colonies. War increased his duties immensely so that Sidney Herbert, going beyond his primary financial role, voluntarily relieved the Duke of many medical issues.

Below this level of authority lay a complex skein of divided responsibility. Military business was conducted by too many offices, all totally separate and independent of each other. The result was inordinate delay and red tape. Independent, but responsible to the civil authorities, were the Commander-in-Chief and the Master-General of the Ordnance. The former was in charge of the infantry and cavalry, and the latter of the artillery and engineers and also of the Ordnance Department, a civil department dealing with the supply and maintenance of artillery and ammunition. The Commissariats, supplying provisions, were a civil department.

Medical matters, for the infantry and for the cavalry, were overall the concern of the Commander-in-Chief, and, for the artillery, the Master-General of the Ordnance. The Board of Ordnance via the Military Secretary was responsible for equipment and hospital stores. Any transport by sea was the responsibility of the Admiralty. Below these various authorities, medical arrangements were in the hands of the Army Medical Department, another civil department. The Director-General of the Army Medical Department, Dr Smith, was not directly responsible to the War Office; instead he was forever dealing with a great many other departments. Like other departments, the medical was constrained in the system of which it was a part, a system which had grown without reasoned arrangement or pruning. At the beginning of the war, to make matters worse, the Medical Departments and the Commissariats, both civil departments with civilian staff, carried less weight than the military departments.

In administering his own department, Smith had directly under his orders a handful of clerks, but otherwise he had little authority though he was responsible for the army hospital services and the doctors working in them. Nor was he even exclusively responsible for the regimental surgeons, who were under the direct command of the Commanding Officer of their regiment and, with two masters, sometimes in a difficult position.[2] With all these difficulties, Smith's whole position was unsatisfactory.

The immediate responsibility for the medical arrangements of the Army of the East was that of the Inspector-General of Hospitals, John Hall, stationed at the army headquarters. Hall was responsible both to Smith and to Lord Raglan, in command of the army, for hospital and medical services generally. Responsible to Hall were Hospital and Divisional medical staffs, and the Regimental Surgeons and Assistant Surgeons who themselves were also responsible to the commanding officers of their regiments.

Throughout the war, Andrew Smith and John Hall faced a barrage of criticism, and were particular objects of Florence Nightingale's scorn. However, late in the war, they were knighted and their reputations have been rehabilitated as men doing their duty in circumstances of extreme difficulty and working within an impossible administrative structure.

In ordinary circumstances, the Regimental Surgeon was in charge of the regimental hospital of 12 beds, with bedding equipment and tentage. His staff consisted of an assistant surgeon, or sometimes two assistant surgeons, regimental orderlies, and 20 stretcher-bearers provided from the regimental bandsmen.[3] Transport was never satisfactory.

Field hospitals were regimental hospitals grouped together. Evacuation from them was to general hospitals well behind the lines. These hospitals were under the command of a combatant officer, sometimes of lower rank than the senior medical officer. Significantly, the senior medical officer had no administrative power beyond strictly medical matters and could do little about buildings, equipment, and diet, or even medical supplies and comforts. His medical staff was made up of several doctors; all other staff had to be obtained from the local military commandant from units under his command. Until Florence Nightingale appeared with her band of nurses, no female nurses had been employed since soon after the Napoleonic wars. The purveyor's department, almost abolished after the Peninsula War, was responsible for hospital equipment. Throughout, there was too much red tape, too many forms, and a degree of financial control that was completely out of place in war time. As usual, Florence Nightingale put the matter in a nutshell, 'the system of checks and counter checks seems to have been invented for the purpose of saving money instead of for that of saving the lives of the sick'.[4]

Besides this administrative tangle, another problem was becoming apparent, shortage of doctors. Existing establishments had been pared down in peacetime, and now, in wartime, more doctors, especially experienced doctors, were needed.

When war came, the regulars were reinforced by volunteers who joined the service as Assistant Surgeons. The applicants were required to be between 21 and 26 years of age, possess certain of the medical diplomas, and undergo examination. However, soon the shortage of doctors became severe and the grade of Acting Assistant Surgeon was created for which the original requirements were relaxed. These were temporary posts, though they could be made permanent. They were filled by patriotic young doctors wishing for further experience, particularly in surgery. More senior applicants had no incentive to apply, while the regulars were anxious about new recruits blocking their promotion.

The army medical services, still looking back to the Peninsular War, were now struggling with more scientific concepts. Doctors, themselves receiving appropriate training according to the best standards of the times, were keeping pace with change. At some medical schools, the subject of military medicine was in the curriculum. Doctors were members of the middle class, professional men aspiring to the standards of the medical profession, a profession only regularised by registration when the Medical Act was passed after the war, in 1858. Their social position had risen since the 18th century but was still somewhat below that of combatant officers who were usually from the aristocracy or landed gentry, and who ordinarily purchased their commissions. Doctors contended that the cost to themselves of their medical training was equivalent. Decorations which invite respect both for their recipients and for the regiments and corps to which they belong were not being given to medical officers. Despite holding equivalent ranks, the medical officer was usually held to be inferior to the most junior combatant officer.[5] The advice of medical officers was often swept aside by their regimental commanding officers, though not for military or tactical reasons; a great commander such as Wellington had trusted the advice of his chief medical officer, Sir James McGrigor.[6] In the regiment, the inferiority of medical men in the social order could lead to a firing party being refused at the burial of a medical officer.[7] Palmerston caused offence when he said that the medical officers in the Crimea did not belong to the aristocracy or gentry,[8] while Florence Nightingale always believed that a doctor should have the weight of a gentleman among gentlemen.[9]

As 1855 opened, no one could say whether casualties would increase, and whether there would be new heights of sickness. With this prospect ahead, the government, faced with a shortage of experienced army doctors, decided not to neglect the services of civil doctors. This, the War Office believed, was the quickest way to address the problem.[10] The idea of civilian doctors was not new. After Waterloo, a great many civil surgeons were sent over to Brussels as the number of army doctors was totally inadequate. The commanding officer of a detachment had, under army regulations, the power to engage a civilian practitioner if his unit was without a Regimental Assistant Surgeon. A few civilian doctors were employed at Scutari in the early part of the war under ad hoc arrangements. Now the aim was to attract experienced doctors, especially to fill more senior positions. The bait was the better rate of pay, the contract limited to the period of the war, and comparatively easily ended, a gratuity at the end, and military discipline at arm's length. Such an appointment could be attractive to a patriotic doctor anxious to enlarge his experience. Persuading Andrew Smith to recruit civilian doctors and the establishment of a civil hospital were to be the next moves. Sidney Herbert was in correspondence with both Andrew Smith (on 24th December 1854 and 19th January 1855), and Florence Nightingale (on 5th March after Herbert had resigned), on the subject of civil hospitals and civil doctors, pointing out that most cases were medical not surgical as expected, and the intention was to avoid employing only raw inexperienced boys.[11] Florence Nightingale wrote, 'I hail the plan of the civil hospital.'[12]

On Jan 22nd 1855, an advertisement appeared asking civilian doctors to volunteer for military service. A week later on 29 January, the Duke of Newcastle, Secretary of State for War, proposed, in the House of Lords, a civil hospital, paid for by the War Office and for the military, but staffed by civilians. Gone would be military red tape and muddled organisation: moreover civilian doctors might easily prove more skilful, particularly surgically, than their military counterparts. On February 7th, Mr Gladstone, as Chancellor of the Exchequer, announced in the Commons that the late Secretary for War (Newcastle) had organised a civil medical establishment which would be sent out immediately.[13] Civil surgeons and civil hospital were to be a short term arrangement, and the suggestion was met with varying enthusiasm and some confusion. There were suspicions that what was being proposed was the command of a military hospital by a civilian, something that resembled French hospital arrangements, then usually admired, but decidedly not in this respect.

Early that year, to meet the need for beds, a hospital at Smyrna intended for convalescents, had been opened and staffed with five army doctors. It was soon grossly overcrowded with the same insanitary conditions as at Scutari.[14] On February 12th, the Cabinet agreed that the hospital should be entirely under the direction of civil medical men, and a party of civilian volunteers drawn from London was sent out. Smyrna became the first Civil Hospital.

Following Roebuck's vote of censure and the defeat of the government on January 26th, the Duke of Newcastle and Sidney Herbert, the two ministers directly responsible for the idea of civilian doctors, were gone; Newcastle resigned immediately after the vote of censure, and Herbert on February 23rd. A letter from Lord Panmure, Newcastle's successor, to the medical press, requested that experienced civil doctors should be seconded from their posts and allowed to return after service which would be for a limited period; more senior doctors would receive £2 2s per diem, and assistants £1 5s per diem, and those in private practice would receive a full year's salary at the end of their service. [15]

Subsequently there was criticism of the way in which the medical staff for the civil hospitals was chosen. In Edinburgh, the entire surgical team of young surgeons, with the exception of Joseph Lister who was a Quaker, volunteered for service as civil surgeons. Clearly Professor Simpson, who had introduced the use of chloroform as an anaesthetic, played an important part in selection, for a curious article dated March 26th 1855 appeared in the Medical Times and Gazette which started with the words:

> Alexander the Great is said to have wept when he had no more worlds to conquer – we wonder if Atlas ever grumbled that he had only the whole world on his shoulders? One would think that, with the large Professional reputation which Professor Simpson enjoys; with the multifarious occupations in which that must involve him; with the duties of preparation for his class, and the necessity of keeping his information up to the present standard, his time must be occupied, or more than occupied. Not so thinks Lord Panmure. The Minister-at-War has commissioned the learned Professor to organize a Staff for a Civil Hospital in the East, to be officered by the Edinburgh school. All this, we believe, came about as follows:- When the wishes and proposals of Government in regard to such institutions became known, a number of the Clerks and Dressers in the Edinburgh Hospital expressed a wish to go, and consulted Dr Christison on the subject, whose son was one of their number. He took the matter up with his usual promptitude and decision, and wrote to Lord Panmure his

> views on the subject. No very satisfactory reply was returned; but a few days afterwards, Dr Simpson, who had meanwhile made one of his flying visits to London, announced that he had received a carte blanche to arrange the whole matter.[16]

The article speculates in a rather cynical manner about various appointments, and ends with: 'We fear the whole conception is a monstrous one, and that the ovum is not unlikely to be blighted.' The phrase was chosen as J.Y. Simpson, a giant on the Edinburgh scene, was Professor of Obstetrics.

Renkioi Hospital was to be the second Civil Hospital, entirely new and purpose built.[17] Smyrna had used existing buildings and repeated many of the mistakes of Scutari. If the necessity arose, Renkioi Hospital could be extended to provide the same accommodation as Scutari, although, since Sir John Pringle's observations in the 18th century, the safety of large hospitals was thought somewhat suspect. The first appointment to the new hospital was that of Dr Edmund Parkes as Medical Superintendent. Parkes received his letter of appointment as Superintendent on March 30 1855 and resigned his appointment at University College Hospital of Professor of Clinical Medicine on the same day. It was believed that, unlike Smyrna, at least two-thirds of the patients would be medical, not surgical, cases.

At the beginning of April, the staff of Renkioi Hospital was announced as follows:

> Physicians. Dr Goodeve M.D., Retired East India Company's Bengal Medical Service; Late Professor in the Medical College, Calcutta, and Physician to the Hospital, Calcutta.
>
> Dr Robertson, M.D., Fellow of the Royal College of Physicians, Edinburgh; Physician to the Royal Infirmary.
>
> Mr J Spencer Wells, Fellow of the Royal College of Surgeons, England; Surgeon to the Civil Hospital, Smyrna; and formerly Surgeon to the Royal Naval Hospital, Malta.
>
> 'For the junior appointments, the applicants were extremely numerous – more than eight hundred – and among them are a number of most able and excellent young men. A staff of Nurses and Lady Nurses is in the course of formation. Mr Humphrey M.R.C.S. ...to undertake the important task of supervising the Apothecaries' department'.

The announcement finished on an optimistic note: 'The staff and arrangements of this new hospital are so good that even those whose special vocation seems to be to find fault, must, we think, acknowledge their excellence'.[18] Unlike previous purely military hospitals, a female nursing staff was engaged from the outset.

In London, Sir James Clark played a large part in setting up the hospital; his strength was his grasp of affairs and he had the ear of the Prince Consort, to whom he was Physician. Later he became 'Physician to Her Majesty'. He was a man to whom statesmen referred in medical matters and, though worldly wise, was noted for his simplicity; he knew where to go for advice and how to sift it. In the Crimean War, 'he was the soul of a sort of semi-official committee which undertook the impromptu supply of nurses, medical men, sick comforts and the like. His judgement and his business habits stood him in good stead; and for some months, during the stress of the national trouble, he worked with the utmost assiduity. His waiting rooms during this time were thronged in the early mornings by nurses and others, of whose fitness for service he was to judge'.[19] He was asked by the Government to undertake the preliminaries of launching Renkioi Hospital.[20] Not only did he undertake the duty of selecting suitable staff and greeting them on their return, but he advised Parkes about setting up the hospital and its operation, help that was warmly acknowledged.[21]

So much for the steps taken to set up the Civil Hospitals, an aim which was rapidly achieved. *The Times*, usually at odds with the government, always supported the idea of the civil hospitals, and its vivid accounts were enthusiastic. Unfortunately, elsewhere, a civilian arrangement was less popular. The reasons were understandable. The Director General, although he needed more doctors, was unenthusiastic about employing civilians, particularly on terms that would arouse the jealousy of the regular staff. At the outset he specified that civil surgeons must have superior qualifications or experience compared to the regulars, and only this would justify a higher rate of pay. The higher wages were not always as straightforward as first imagined, for the staff at Smyrna waited long for the promised payment of their severance gratuity of one year's pay.[22]

The rates of pay for Civil Surgeons were bound to be a source of jealousy to the regular army doctor. The remuneration of Civil Surgeons at £766.10s per annum or £456. 5s per annum for an Assistant Surgeon was much better than that of medical officers in the regular army (Table 1).

Table 1 Army Medical Officers' Pay

Grade	<10 yrs	10-20 yrs	20-25 yrs	>25 yrs
Ass't Surgeon	£136.17s	£182.10s	£182.10s	£182.10s
Regimental Surgeon & Staff Surgeon 2nd Class	£237.5s	£273.15s	£346.15s	£401.10s
Staff Surgeon		£346.15s	£401.10s	£438
Deputy Inspector General		£438.00	£511	£547.10s
Inspector-General		£657	£693.10s	£730
Director-General		£1,200		

Source: Pinkoffs P. *Experiences of a Civilian in Eastern Military Hospitals*, 163. London: Williams & Norgate, 1857.

Of course, for the Civil Surgeon there was no half pay or pension (which for an Assistant Surgeon in the army only amounted to 13/- a day) but, on discharge, there was to be full pay for a year which would cover loss of earnings from private practice. These rates can be compared with those of the unskilled 'navigators' of the Army Work Corps, who received 30s per week or the net pay as major of a brigade on active service of about £400 per annum.[23]

Civil Surgeons were only appointed on the recommendation of a respected medical referee; they held ranks equivalent to service ranks, did not wear an established uniform and were, like their military counterparts, addressed as 'Doctor'. Many were employed as physicians, not surgeons, though officially designated Civil Surgeon. The intention was that the civil doctors should form the staff of entirely civil hospitals, i.e. be segregated, but when the civil doctors found their services were more urgently needed at Scutari and in the Crimea, some volunteered to serve there. The army doctors' feelings usually changed when Civil Surgeons volunteered to work side by side with them in the Crimea. Military discipline was not a burden to the Civil Surgeon working in a Civil Hospital but, in the army hospital, life could be frustrating.[24]

Dr Parkes, after the war, in his Report on Renkioi Hospital, put the intention as, 'to officer this hospital with civil medical practitioners instead of calling upon the already overburthened army medical officers to undertake the duties'. However the experiment of a civil hospital had another altogether different advantage. The need to circumvent red tape was painfully obvious. When Florence Nightingale was sent to the Crimea, it was an entirely new departure and she reported directly to Sidney Herbert. When some hospital equipment at Scutari was needed, the Secretary of State for War asked, via the Foreign Office and contrary to the ordinary military practice of ordering through the Purveyor's department, that it should be obtained by the British Ambassador, Lord Stratford de Redcliffe.[25] Again Andrew Smith, the Director-General in London, arranged that Dr Menzies, in medical charge of the base hospital at Scutari, should send reports to him direct without going through Hall, his immediate superior.[26] By creating and administering a civil hospital, the War Office could bypass the army and its attendant red tape and oversee the project directly.

[1] Sweetman J. *War and Administration. The Significance of the Crimean War for the British Army.* Edinburgh: Scottish Academic Press, 1984.

[2] *The army surgeons in the Crimea*. Lancet 1856. 1.101.

[3] Cantlie N. *History of the Army Medical Department*. 2.10. Edinburgh London: Churchill Livingstone, 1974.

[4] *Royal Commission... Sick and Wounded* 1858. Q10051.

[5] *Lancet* 1856; 1:435-6. James Syme, the surgeon (Chapter 7), was advised not to apply for a patent for a solvent for caoutchouc, which, at the age of 18 he had discovered (predating the process used in making 'macintoshes') because it would indicate an interest in 'trade'. Obituary. *British Medical Journal* 1870; 2:21-26.

[6] Howard M. *Wellington's Doctors. The British Army Medical Services in the Napoleonic Wars*. 87. Staplehurst: Spellmount, 2002.

[7] *Royal Commission... sick and wounded* 1858. Q9962-3.

[8] *The medical officers in the Crimea and Lord Palmerston. Medical Times and Gazette*. 1855; 10:328.

[9] Woodham-Smith C. *Florence Nightingale 1820-1910*. 399. London: Constable, 1950.

[10] *Parliamentary Papers*. 1856 XIII Proceedings of the Select Committee of the Medical Department (Army).

[11] Lord Stanmore. *Sidney Herbert. Lord Herbert of Lea*. 1: 399. London: John Murray. 1906.

[12] Goldie SM. *Florence Nightingale. Letters from the Crimea 1854-1856*, 89:119. Manchester: Mandolin, 1997.
[13] *Hansard* 7 Feb 1855.1319.
[14] Shepherd J. *Crimean Doctors*. 2:424; Liverpool: Liverpool University Press, 1991.
[15] Anonymous. *The Civil Hospitals and the War.* Lancet 1855; 1:226.
[16] *Provincial Correspondence. Civil Hospitals in the East. Medical Times & Gazette* 1855; 10:317.
[17] Recent descriptions of Renkioi Hospital include those of Shepherd J. *Crimean Doctors*, 1991: Silver CP. *Brunel's Crimean War Hospital – Renkioi revisited. Journal of Medical Biography* 1998; 6:234-239 and 2000; 8:183: Silver CP. *Renkioi: A forgotten Crimean War Hospital and its significance.* Vesalius 2004; 10:55-60: Kentley E. ed. *Isambard Kingdom Brunel. Recent Works*, 2000.
[18] *Medical Times and Gazette* 1855; 10:342.
[19] *British Medical Journal* 1870; 2:53-54.
[20] *Proceedings of the Royal Society* 1871; 19:xiii-xix.
[21] Parkes EA. *Report on the Formation and General Management of Renkioi Hospital on the Dardanelles, Turkey.* War Department 1857.23. Henceforth *Parkes EA Report...Renkioi Hospital.*
[22] *Case of four Senior Medical Officers of the late Smyrna Hospital. Lancet* 1856; 2:54.
[23] TNA. WO. 43/988.
[24] Pinkoffs P. *Experiences of a Civilian in Eastern Military Hospitals*. 52-58. London: Williams & Norgate, 1857.
[25] Cantlie N. *History of the Army Medical Department*. 2:70-71. London: Churchill Livingstone, 1974.
[26] Cantlie N. *History of the Army Medical Department*. 2:70. London: Churchill Livingstone, 1974.

Figure 6: Isambard Kingdom Brunel by Robert Howlett, published by London Stereoscopic & Photographic Company albumen carte-de-visite, November 1857.
Courtesy of the National Portrait Gallery, London

Chapter 4

Brunel and his Plans

I.K. Brunel
1859
Inscription, Royal Albert Bridge, Saltash

On Jan 5th 1855, the Duke of Newcastle wrote to Lord George Paulet, the newly appointed Military Commandant on the Bosphorus and in charge of the hospitals at Scutari.[1] To increase the number of hospital beds, he gave Paulet the choice of opening a new hospital at Kulleli or elsewhere, or opening temporary buildings close to existing hospitals. Better accommodation for convalescence was needed too as the hulks moored in the Bosphorus, and used for convalescent patients, did little to speed recovery. With so many infected wounds, convalescence was often very prolonged, of many months duration. A convalescent hospital at Rhodes, with its healthy climate, or at Smyrna, less attractive but a place of great trade, making supplies easier, should be considered. He advised Paulet to go to see the temporary hospitals erected by the French in the Seraglio gardens (of which Spencer Wells did not think highly[2]). No application for labour was to be made to the Turkish authorities, and work should be started with a force of workmen directly under Paulet's charge. Carpenters from England would be sent out. Thus plans were set in train for more beds, beds for convalescence perhaps very far afield, and for temporary wooden huts with a hint of prefabrication. No reference to civil hospitals was made.

About the same time, because of his first-hand experience, George Macleod, the young surgeon who had just returned to England after visiting the Crimea, was invited by Sidney Herbert, the Secretary at War, to give an account of what he had seen. One matter which they discussed was the way the wounded were housed. Macleod suggested the use of huts similar to ones that had been used in Glasgow in the treatment of a cholera epidemic.[3] He always remained a strong advocate of the hutted hospital.[4]

Newcastle's suggestion to Lord Paulet, about enlarging hospital accommodation by adding huts to existing hospitals, soon developed into a proposal for a complete hutted hospital. Sidney Herbert, assisting Newcastle, had written to Newcastle on January 3rd supplying him with much of the information which Newcastle then passed on as instructions to Paulet. Herbert then wrote separately to Paulet, 'they tell me the French temporary hospitals are very good buildings made of wood and battened and plastered inside: each building holds fifty sick. This is the usual style of Turkish building, which they are therefore used to making. What the French have done we can do.' He continued that wards could be larger but must have sufficient ventilation, and could share services with an adjoining barracks.[5] Britain did do better, and the War Office did not have far to look when the erection of a new hospital overseas, rather than the conversion of an existing building, was decided upon. The man who was to realise these intentions was Isambard Kingdom Brunel.

Brunel was just such an authority as the government needed to ensure success. The Under-Secretary of State for War, Benjamin Hawes (1797-1862), was married to Brunel's sister, and the War Office negotiations lay in his hands and probably started as private conversations between them. This accounted for the extraordinary speed with which Brunel was able to act. Hawes would have been aware of all recent debate at the War Office and could ensure continuity during the changes in ministerial office arising from Roebuck's vote of censure. The new hospital was to be a War Office experiment and unconnected with the Army Medical Department. Hawes may have proposed sending a hospital to Turkey but Brunel himself may have first brought the idea up. For a man who suggested a floating siege gun mounted on a jet-propelled hull which was submerged, the despatch of a prefabricated hospital would not have seemed a flight of fancy.

Hawes had married Sophia, Brunel's sister, in 1820, so that Hawes and Brunel were not only brothers-in-law but close friends over a long period. William Hawes, Benjamin's younger brother, was also a great friend and it was the brothers who introduced Isambard to his wife, Mary, of the musical and talented Horsley family. Their marriage took place in 1836. Benjamin Hawes' closeness to the Brunel family is not in doubt. Hawes was a supporter of the Thames Tunnel of which Isambard's father, Marc, was the engineer. In 1821, Marc Brunel was thrown into prison for debt but after some months, at the instance of many influential friends, he obtained a grant from the government and was liberated. With this in mind, in 1836, Hawes wrote a pamphlet, 'The abolition of arrest and imprisonment for debt considered in six letters'. Hawes had interested himself in the battle of the railway gauges, a subject which was to haunt Brunel, and over Renkioi Hospital he gave Brunel the strongest support. To Isambard Brunel, Hawes was a longstanding friend, to Florence Nightingale, an obstruction.[6]

On 16 Feb 1855, Brunel was asked to undertake the project by Sidney Herbert, still Secretary at War; he agreed on the same day.[7] Right at the start he set out his plans with wonderful clarity, and they were exactly followed.[8]

Brunel was at the height of his career, then 49 years of age, and completing his work on railways in the south west of England. He had met enormous engineering challenges with outstanding originality and boldness, and been responsible for the construction of many miles of railway. His name is ever associated with the Great Western Railway. In October 1835, at a meeting of the directors of the Great Western Railway, one of those present spoke of the enormous length of the proposed railway from London to Bristol. Brunel exclaimed, 'Why not make it longer, and have a steamboat to go from Bristol to New York, and call it the Great Western?' At first treated as a joke, the construction of the great ship, S.S. Great Western, followed. On its maiden voyage, Brunel was very fortunate to escape death in a perilous fall.[9] After S.S. Great Western, he had been responsible for the construction of another great steamship, the Great Britain, and when Renkioi Hospital was being built was engaged on a third, even larger, the Great Eastern, the largest ship in the world. Another project with which he was engaged was the Royal Albert Bridge, Saltash. Just when Brunel was accepting responsibility for Renkioi Hospital, the huge centre pier of the bridge had been sunk into its upright position, a very difficult task needing great engineering skills.

Saltash Bridge was Brunel's last great feat of railway engineering, and he was now entering the last phase of his extremely active and well documented life. His rise to fame was based on his extraordinary capacity for hard work, his persistence, his attention to detail and clear instructions, his excellent draftsmanship, and his charm. He was personally courageous. When he was young, 'whether in boating, in pic-nic parties, or in private theatricals, he was always the life and soul of the party... the invariable leader in every amusement or sport in which he took part'. His methods at work were well known. His offices occupied the ground floor of his home, 19 Duke Street, Westminster, and he employed a staff of about thirty.[10] Brunel would sketch out his ideas and then send these sketches to be turned into engineering drawings. Not all his ambitious projects had been successful, and his career had been clouded by some setbacks of which the railway broad gauge (a failure in that it was not adopted in place of the existing standard gauge), and his completely unsuccessful atmospheric railway are the best known. Soon after Renkioi, he was to be involved in the difficult launch of the Great Eastern, and his falling out with his partner, Scott Russell, the naval architect.[11]

This is the picture that Brunel presented to the world, confirmed by the recollections of his son and other accounts.[12] [13] A recent biography has gone beyond explaining Brunel on the strength of his extraordinary achievements, and instead drawn a picture of a complex and sometimes troubled man, the darker side to his character.[14] Because he applied himself so completely to a project he felt that responsibility for an enterprise and its success were his alone and should be seen as such. He was inclined to feel that all who worked with him, worked for him. He could not delegate, and his team was made up of assistants who were in awe of him. Obstinacy could lead him to reject opinions more soundly based than his own. Yet he was brilliantly capable, so is all this so remarkable? Finally and less defensible, he was niggardly in arranging the payment of contractors who had completed their work, so that they were for ever putting up with disputed or delayed payment.

No dark clouds appear to have hung over the Renkioi project which must have seemed, in many ways, straightforward; he was the sole author, and there was only acclaim by the press. Renkioi can be considered an architectural as well as an engineering project; Brunel had had extensive experience of working with architects on railway buildings, notably at Paddington station, and had himself undertaken the building of the workmen's cottages at Steventon. Any architectural requirements at Renkioi were well within his capabilities. The project was a comparatively simple one, presenting nothing of the complexity and risks of the Saltash Bridge. Planning and ordering of parts had been his responsibility, but its passage to the Dardanelles and its erection, although subject to his instructions, was not solely his; the person in the most powerful position to make sure that the aims were achieved was his own brother-in-law, Benjamin Hawes.

In John Brunton, his assistant on site, Brunel chose an excellent engineer to carry out his instructions, with whom he was always on good terms, so that the shadows which fell across other projects did not do so over Renkioi.

When faced with the challenge of building a hospital, Brunel himself wrote, 'and have obtained, from the best sources within my reach and by personal examination of the London Hospitals, information as to the requirements of such buildings...'.[15] It is known that he met Dr Parkes and corresponded with him to ensure the efficient working of the water closets which Brunel proposed to install.[16] Later in a letter to John Brunton, Brunel wrote: '...You are most fortunate in having exactly the man in Dr Parkes that I should have selected – an enthusiastic clever agreeable man – devoted to the object of understanding plans and works and quite disposed to attach as much importance to the perfection of the building and all those points I deem important as to mere doctoring...'[17] Ventilation and sanitation are constructional concerns, and Brunel was guided by views about health that had come to the fore by the middle of the nineteenth century. He met Sir James Clark and other medical men and was in a position to receive advice from an enormous range of colleagues and contacts. Lastly, Brunel must have been influenced by newspaper reports of conditions overseas during the terrible first winter of the war. He must too have been conversant with the horrible smells, poor sanitation, and closed windows which characterised not only hospital wards but the homes of poorer people as well. At Fort Pitt Military Hospital at Chatham, the cesspools could be smelt a quarter of a mile away. However he wished he knew more of the sort of patients he was catering for.

In planning the hospital, Brunel showed an extraordinary grasp of principles in an unfamiliar situation. He set out the engineering aspects of the hospital in a section of the Renkioi Report published in 1857. The considerations which guided Brunel were:

1) the need to make sick soldiers comfortable. The public now appreciated the soldiers' merits and their hardships.
2) the huge amount of sickness, particularly diarrhoeal diseases. The problem of the sick exceeded even that of caring for the wounded.
3) the importance of ensuring a good water supply, effective sanitation, ventilation, proper cooking facilities, warmth and shelter in clean surroundings.

Taking all these points into consideration, Brunel achieved his aims in ingenious and up-to-date ways. His letters indicate his grasp of the requirements to be met, and his detailed solution to each problem.

Brunel decided to build a hospital using prefabricated parts, and shipping these from England for assembly on site in Turkey. This decision avoided all the hazards of converting an unsatisfactory existing building overseas, or of constructing one anew with the attendant difficulties of using local materials and labour. He next decided upon wood as the material to be used. Brunel himself had great experience in the use of wood as well of iron and steel. He had employed wood in the construction of railway bridges and, departing from Stephenson's practice, used wood rather than stone for railway sleepers. Accepting the comfort and cleanliness of the patients as guiding premises, he proposed a building scheme which could be easily altered and extended as desired. He took cost into account but did not hesitate to recommend expenditure to achieve the standards he thought necessary.

Brunel was well aware of prefabrication as an engineering practice. A huge prefabricated engineering project had just been transported to the Crimea and assembled on site, in a military setting. Early in December 1854, the Duke of Newcastle authorised the construction of a railway at Balaklava, and over the next few weeks 1800 tons of rails and fastenings, 6000 sleepers, 600 tons of timber, and a further 2000 tons of miscellaneous equipment were dispatched in eight ships to Balaklava. A large workforce of navvies, to build the railway, was shipped from England, an important difference from the workforce to be later employed at Renkioi. This railway, besides carrying supplies, arms and ammunition was also used to carry wounded.[18]

In designing Renkioi Hospital, Brunel had only to look to Joseph Paxton (1801-1865), another extraordinary Victorian, whom he already knew and who had begun his career as Head Gardener to the Duke of Devonshire at Chatsworth. Early examples of prefabrication, not in engineering but as a building practice, were the small prefabricated garden buildings and greenhouses which were already on the market in the middle of the century. Advertisements for these, every part fixed and marked before being packed, and to be sent to all parts of the United Kingdom, appeared in *The Gardener's Chronicle*. The advertisements were directed to the nobility and gentry, but Joseph Paxton, the founder of the *Chronicle*, dreamed of glasshouses by the million. Prefabricated houses were dispatched to the colonies, and an iron building was sent out in parts to the Crimea by Mowbray Morris, the Times Manager, for the use of William Howard Russell.[19] Paxton himself employed prefabrication in its most striking form when building the Great Exhibition of 1851, in effect a gigantic conservatory, subsequently moved to become the Crystal Palace at Sydenham. Brunel was on the building committee and advised important modifications to the design. After the move to Sydenham, he was responsible for the design and construction of two water towers there.[20]

A prefabricated hospital of any substance had never been built, but prefabricated wooden huts were shipped to the Crimea when it was discovered how badly the troops needed shelter. The Editor of the *Times*, J D Delane, made a visit which started in Constantinople at the beginning of August and finished in the Crimea, so that he was home by early October. On his return he lobbied the Duke of Newcastle and 'urged the provision of wooden huts for the troops who would have to face the rigours of a winter in the East, pointing out that the work might be done expeditiously at Constantinople, where all the houses were built of wood, and where labour was both cheap and plentiful.'[21]

As soon as it was known that the army would have to winter in the Crimea, Lord Raglan despatched ships to scour the shores of the Black Sea for timber, as the fighting zone had been denuded of timber for fuel. This timber was landed at the small port of Balaklava and was used for providing protection for men, horses, and stores. Eleven shipments were made, but unfortunately uprights and beams (scantlings), and planks, were not in the right proportion in the individual loads and it was a month before the timber from the first ship to arrive, the Sea Nymph, could be assembled with other appropriate timber. The space required to store 77672 planks and 19434 scantling pieces at a small port, their safekeeping during the winter, and the task of transporting them, proved to be problems which had never been considered. About the middle of November, contracts in Britain were entered into for the supply of wooden huts for the army, to be sent in finished parts so that, with the aid of printed directions and lithographed plans which accompanied them, they could be put together even by unskilled workmen. Each of these huts measured 28 feet long, 16 feet wide, and 11 to 12 feet high, the roof sloping to side walls 6 feet high. They were much smaller than those at Renkioi and much less well constructed. Boards 3/4 to 1 inch thick were used for the walls while thicker boards made up a slightly sloping floor which left space down the centre of the hut for a stove for cooking and heating. Under Crimean conditions, space was sufficient for 20 or 25 men, half that number in more favourable conditions. The first batch was landed at Balaklava on January 1st, the first ten huts issued on January 5th and, with the exception of 50 huts for officers, all, some 1400, were issued by May 21st. Each hut weighed 2 ½ tons. Lord Raglan was said to have appropriated 270 mules for conveyance but as mules were not referred to again, no transport can have been available. By this stage of the winter, the roads and tracks had become a sea of mud, and disease and semi-starvation meant that soldiers could carry no more than 20 to 25 lbs each. It was calculated that for one hut to reach the front, 250 to 300 men were needed. There were too few, and arriving in mid-winter, those which were delivered were generally erected close to the port. One hundred heavier huts, obtained from Trieste, proved even more difficult to handle. By great exertion, a few huts were got up to the front line and, at first earmarked for the wounded, were the first hospital huts, albeit small.[22] These were lessons to profit from.

Napoleon III was interested in wooden buildings for the French army, and by December 1854 a demonstration hut made by the firm of Eassie of Gloucester (which manufactured the Renkioi huts), had been erected for him in the grounds of the palace at Versailles.[23] Later, prefabricated buildings for special uses, e.g. prefabricated (metal) churches and at least one example of a specifically designed hospital hut appeared in commercial catalogues.[24]

With climatic conditions in mind, Brunel imagined the hospital translated to Turkey but he was quite unaware as to where it would be placed. He simply specified that a suitable site must be found. The parts must be easily delivered to a site which would be spacious enough to house all the buildings, have access to a satisfactory water supply, and allow the installation of sanitation. Of course the district should also be thought generally healthy. He specified all these requirements in a letter to Hawes, long before any move was made.[25] Such a site was found, and those in Turkey were to obey his instructions implicitly.

Brunel visualised the hospital being set up on any suitable site, with sufficient huts (or wards) of identical design, to provide the number of beds required. The individual ward hut for 50 patients was the central element of Brunel's plan, an element which could be repeated as often as required. Each wooden hut measured 100 feet long, 40 feet wide, and 25 feet high. Although large in comparison with other army huts, the dimensions of the huts were small enough for them to be sited on sloping ground (if necessary across the direction of the slope). Each prefabricated part was light enough to be carried by two men. Besides the huts, enormous quantities of supplies were to be sent, consisting of other buildings such as the cookhouses and laundries (metal because of the risk of fire), a railway, and all the other equipment needed. Brunel arranged that the cargoes should be made up in such a way that the loss of one ship with its cargo would not jeopardise the construction of all the huts but have only a limited effect. A specimen hut for inspection was erected at Paddington station in the middle of March 1855.

Simplicity of construction was a necessity, and Brunel had almost perforce to use single storey buildings which would occupy a large site. He proposed setting out the wards, following what later came to be known as the 'pavilion principle', with individual units widely spaced, the huts being arranged in rows, in a circle or irregularly.[26] Renkioi could have just as aptly been described as built on the 'barrack principle', though no such category exists, but it was undoubtedly a pavilion hospital built when this idea was emerging. The wards were quite separate from administrative and other buildings. With windows set high along both sides of the hut and opening on to wide open spaces, lighting and cross ventilation would be satisfactory and in accord with Florence Nightingale's subsequently well known views.[27] Brunel, proclaiming himself a monomaniac for fresh air for invalids, allowed some 1200 cu. ft. of air per patient, approaching that of a civilian hospital such as the London Hospital where the allowance was about 1700 cu. ft.[28] Medical officers customarily liked more than 1000 cu. ft., much more than 306 cu. ft., the allowance in the Camp General Hospital, or 373 cu. ft. in the highly regarded Castle Hospital, both in the Crimea.[29] Brunel also designed a special system of forced ventilation (Chapter 6). By making effective ventilation a prerequisite, Brunel was following the views of health reformers. Hospitals, schools, and ships carrying emigrants to outposts of the Empire, were all being scrutinised on this account. The window tax was repealed in 1851. Brunel believed that even if the wards became overcrowded, ventilation would still be adequate.

Brunel however went further than fresh air, a topic soon thought to be exaggerated, and set about improving other sanitary arrangements. Each hut was to be connected with the water supply and main drainage system. For cooking, ablutions, and sanitation, a supply of running water would be essential. A satisfactory water supply and effective sanitation were much in the public mind. The Parliamentary Commission on cholera was sitting and produced its report in 1855; one finding was that the water supply of the metropolis exerted a great influence on the spread of cholera.[30] John Snow's view, that cholera was water-borne and its prevention dependent on the purity of water supply, was frequently expressed in the medical press. For Renkioi, Brunel proposed a safe water supply and 'water closets instead of any other contrivance because there are no equally easy means of securing any certainty of comfort and cleanliness and these are very easy means of obtaining these essentials at a trifling cost'.[31] With 'the prevalent diseases likely to be attended with diarrhoea', he considered them imperative. The use of water closets with drainage into sewers rather than cesspits had been increasingly developed. The first water closet at the London Hospital had been installed at the end of the eighteenth century but these were not siphoning water closets.[32] The first public lavatories were the greatly improved Jennings syphon water closets installed at the Great Exhibition in 1851; similar water closets were soon installed at railway stations.[33] Pan water closets were recommended by the Sanitary Commission but they did not arrive at Scutari until some six months after siphon water closets were installed at Renkioi. The Metropolitan Water Board was formed in 1855, and soon after, at an estimated cost of £1,500,000, the construction by Bazalgette of the Great Sewer and drainage system of London was begun.

Design, careful construction, and the provision of stoves ensured that the huts would be warm and comfortable. Brunel was saved the trouble of designing cooking stoves himself for he met Alexis Soyer, before Soyer left London to supervise the kitchens at Scutari, and agreed to use stoves of his design.[34]

Brunel brooked no delay, and proceeded with his plans at a lightning pace, pausing only long enough to take careful soundings about what was needed, which unavoidably consumed valuable time. Some three weeks after accepting his task, Brunel was writing to complain of the slowness of decision and to ask for authority to make arrangements with contractors and order at once items such as boilers which took a long time to construct. He gave instructions himself for buying the materials required and, after saying that these buildings, 'if wanted at all must be wanted before they can possibly arrive', replied to criticisms with, 'Such a course may possibly be unusual in the execution of Government work – but it involves only an amount of responsibility which men in my profession are accustomed to take... it is only by prompt & independent actions of a single individual entrusted with such powers that expedition can be secured, and vexatious and mischievous delays avoided...[35]

Having decided upon his plans, Brunel's task was to find an engineer he could trust to carry out his instructions. He chose John Brunton (1812-1899), the son of one of his previous rivals. Brunton became Brunel's representative, and responsible to him, though not his but a government employee.

John Brunton recorded, for his grandchildren, his memories in a delightful diary or 'Book', a handwritten account of his life up to his return from India in 1865.[36] Brunton's 'Book', written when he was old, was intended for his young readers, and accuracy sometimes faltered. Once he referred to 1600 patients in the hospital, far in excess of the real maximum, but what excitement his account of murderous Bashi-Bazouks must have given.

Brunton describes how Brunel summoned him. He was working for Hutchinson and Ritson, engineering contractors, as engineering adviser, and had been involved in several other contracts where Brunel was consulting engineer. He was therefore well known to Brunel. While living at Dorchester and working on the construction of the Wilts, Somerset and Weymouth Railway, he received a telegram from Brunel bidding him to come at once by the night mail for an interview. He set off and at 6.0 a.m. presented himself at Brunel's office, 19 Duke Street, Westminster. He had a short and somewhat intimidating interview with Brunel, and then gives a wonderful account of how he next visited Mr Hawes at the War Office and refused to accept the post and responsibility of building the hospital unless he were given carte blanche. After appearing to turn him down, Mr Hawes capitulated at a second meeting and he was appointed with all his stipulations to avoid red-tape accepted. There was no time for any delay, and a week later he started an eventful journey. Snow delayed him and, to catch the train, he had to go down the Thames by boat from Hungerford Stairs, after bribing the helmsman of the otherwise empty steamer to make the journey.

Brunton was instructed to go first to Smyrna to supervise the improvements needed to turn a Turkish barracks into a satisfactory hospital. In his diary he says that, before leaving England, he had spent £25,000, in the course of a week, for supplies for the hospital. He does not mention that the hospital had recently been inspected by Dr Sutherland of the Sanitary Commission.[37] On arrival, he found the barracks indescribably filthy and insanitary. He effected great improvements but the building was never satisfactory. He was then ordered to Constantinople to meet Parkes. While there he met Florence Nightingale and found her a 'wonderful business-like woman'. He told her about Miss Stanley and what her 'lady' nurses were doing at Smyrna. Lady nurses were educated women from a higher social class than ordinary nurses. They were often unpaid and with a limited knowledge of nursing. Miss Nightingale was against lady nurses, as opposed to trained nurses. Brunton was not to know that the arrival, against her wishes, of Miss Stanley and her party had proved a great trial for Florence Nightingale.[38]

It was the responsibility of Dr Parkes to select the hospital site, but Brunel, though far away, played the greatest part in determining where it was built. Brunel in his letter to Hawes on 28 February 1855 stated the site requirements: an almost flat area, close to shipping, with an ample water supply and, implicitly, in healthy surroundings. These requirements could not be varied and, although they may not seem particularly difficult to achieve, the need for a large water supply which was essential for Brunel's plans, decided the hospital's site. Parkes arrived in Constantinople on 18th April 1855 and started his search at once. In this he was assisted by John Brunton, the engineer, and Mr Jenner, who was to be Purveyor at Renkioi and was the brother of Dr William Jenner, Parkes' colleague at University College Hospital. He had received advice from several sources at Constantinople; the Ambassador, Commandant, army medical officers, three local medical practitioners, including an Armenian educated in Edinburgh, and interpreters. In his Report, he gives a very clear account of the considerations which determined his choice. An initial plan to extend Scutari, militarily far the most suitable site, had to be rejected because of lack of space. The banks of the Bosphorus were too steep, a succession of limestone ridges without level ground on the top; while on nearby Princes Island (Prinkipo) the water supply was defective.[39] Parkes also considered the coastline of the Black Sea and Sea of Marmora. Sinope was a possibility, a tiny peninsula on the southern shore of the Black Sea, where in November 1853, the Turkish fleet had been destroyed by the Russian fleet. Some 200 miles from the Crimea, at first thought it seemed more favourably placed in some respects than even Scutari. For this reason it would have been the first choice of Dr John Hall, Inspector General of Hospitals and the senior medical officer to the Army in the East. As no Naval vessel could be made available, it was only possible for Parkes to visit Sinope on a commercial steamer, and he calculated that to do this would mean his being away three weeks. The ships carrying the hospital were already approaching the Dardanelles so there was little time to reach a decision. Apart from other considerations, had there been delay in unloading, demurrage of £1000 a day would have been payable.[40] He rejected Sinope because he did not know whether a suitable site with a good water supply for the hospital could be found there, it was not on any frequent commercial steamer route, and it would not receive mail or supplies readily from Constantinople, 350 miles away by sea passage.

In his 'Book', Brunton tells of his own journey. First he went east along the shore of the Black Sea towards Trebizond, and then, after luckily escaping serious injury when he fell from a mule, along the southern shore of the Sea of Marmara. In the whole diary, Parkes is only mentioned twice and indeed the construction of Renkioi hospital is hardly referred to. The impression is given that choosing the site was Brunton's doing alone. He said, without mentioning Parkes, that he then found 'a splendid site combining all my requirements' at Renkioi, drew up his report and sent it to Constantinople, immediately receiving instructions to proceed. However it is clear that Parkes, Brunton, and Jenner set out for the Dardanelles on 30 April and, with help from Frederick Calvert, the British Consul at Dardanelles who had a perfect knowledge of the country, together found an ideal site on the Dardanelles. Unlike the Black Sea coast, the area was familiar to the British authorities in Constantinople. The site was a very gradually sloping shelf on which the hospital could be built close to the sea with a daily supply of 25,000 gallons of water available, which the novel modern sanitation with water closets and sewers demanded. It was here, close to Erenkioi, a village of 3000 inhabitants, mostly Greek, that Renkioi Hospital was finally built. Brunton had been in constant touch with Brunel,[41] and the site satisfied all his criteria and moreover lay directly on the busiest of shipping routes so communications were good. Compared to Sinope it had the advantage of being to the west of the bottleneck caused by the persistent adverse winds at the Narrows of the Dardanelles. These would have delayed sailing ships carrying the hospital parts so that a journey from the Dardanelles to Sinope could have taken as long as that from England to the Dardanelles. The suitability of the site, safer transport of patients than in earlier days, and the faint possibility of operations at the mouth of the Danube, had all swayed the decision.[42]

Parkes considered that if, as had been suggested, further prefabricated hospitals were needed then Sinope might be a suitable choice later and he arranged for a more junior doctor, Dr Cowan, to visit Sinope, and assess it, and then to see Dr Hall. Dr Cowan considered that the water supply in summer was likely to be inadequate. Dr Hall was not helpful and subsequently expressed himself bitterly about the Renkioi site. A 500-bedded Turkish military hospital was later sited at Sinope but was said not to have been much used as it was rather out of the way.[43] Hall in his original recommendation of Sinope was oblivious of doubts about the water supply. When considering siting hospital huts at the Monastery Hospital in the Crimea, he mentions, without comment, that water could be drawn from the fountain within the precincts of the monastery itself, or from the well in front of the outbuildings, a far cry from the supply that Renkioi demanded.[44] After the War, he emphasised the great cost of the elaborate water supply at Renkioi.

Brunel, in letters to Brunton, was glad that Scutari had not been chosen, acclaimed the site at Renkioi, and later wrote that he was pleased that another plan to send some huts to Smyrna had not been followed.[45]

[1] TNA. WO 33/01.

[2] Wells TS. *Preparations for the Sick and Wounded of our Crimean Army. Medical Times & Gazette* 1855; 10:648-50.

[3] Obituary *British Medical Journal* 1892; 2:637.

[4] *The Construction of Hospitals. British Medical Journal* 1869; 2:221. Macleod had 'submitted plans for hospitals such as were afterwards used in the Dardanelles, and he could say, from his own experience of huts and tents in the treatment of the wounded, that nothing could be more perfect'.

[5] Lord Stanmore. Sydney Herbert. *Lord Herbert of Lea*. 1:389. London: John Murray, 1906.

[6] Cook ET. *The Life of Florence Nightingale*. 1.403. London: Macmillan, 1913. General Lefroy, close friend and adviser of Florence Nightingale, described Hawes as 'a third rate politician, who appointed to his office knew nothing of military matters, and had not a statesmanlike grasp of the subject'.

[7] Rolt LTC. *Isambard Kingdom Brunel.* 293. Harmondsworth: Penguin Books, 1970.
[8] Parkes EA. *Report...Renkioi Hospital.* Appendix 39-44.
[9] Brunel I. *The Life of Isambard Kingdom Brunel.* 233, 242. London: Longmans Green, 1870.
[10] Brindle S. *Brunel. The man who built the world.* 230-231. London: Weidenfeld and Nicholson, 2005.
[11] Rolt LTC. *Isambard Kingdom Brunel* 326. Harmondsworth: Penguin Books, 1970.
[12] Brunel I. *The Life of Isambard Kingdom Brunel.* London: Longmans Green, 1870.
[13] Noble Celia Brunel. *The Brunels. Father and Son.* London: Cobden-Sanderson, 1938.
[14] Vaughan A. *Isambard Kingdom Brunel. Engineering Knight Errant.* London: John Murray, 1991.
[15] *Brunel Letter Book 12.* P126. IKB to Benjamin Hawes 22 Feb 1855. Bristol University Library.
[16] *Brunel Letter Book 12.* IKB to Dr Parkes 13 Apr 1855. Bristol University Library.
[17] *Brunel Letter Book 12.* P.164 IKB to John Brunton 2 Apr 1855. Bristol University Library.
[18] Cooke B. *The Grand Crimean Central Railway.* 2nd Edition. Knutsford: Cavalier House, 1997.
[19] *History of the Times. Vol 2* 1841-1884.183. London. Times. 1939.
[20] Brunel I. *The Life of Isambard Kingdom Brunel.* 448. London: Longmans Green, 1870.
[21] Dasent AI. *James Thadeus Delane. Editor of the Times.* 1.196. London: John Murray. 1908.
[22] *Report of the Commission of Inquiry into the Supplies of the British Army in the Crimea.* 2nd Report 33-37. June 1855.
[23] *Gloucester Chronicle* 2 Dec 1854.
[24] Gilbert H. *Prefabricated Structures for the Crimean War.* Israel: Technion, 1972.
[25] Brunel *Letter Book 12.* IKB to Benjamin Hawes. 28 Feb 1855. Bristol University Library.
[26] Renkioi, an early example of a hospital on the 'pavilion plan', has attracted no attention on this account. The Royal Naval Hospital at Plymouth (1758-62), the first 'pavilion plan' hospital, was followed by the Blackburn Infirmary started in 1858 after the Crimean War. Renkioi Hospital was designed ahead of the generation of permanent hospitals of this type, of which St. Thomas' Hospital in London was the best known example. The 'pavilion plan', favoured by Florence Nightingale, was popular for many years until changing circumstances led to other layouts.
[27] Nightingale F. *Notes on Hospitals.* London: Parker, 1859.

[28] *Royal Commission... Sick and Wounded 1858*. Q1509.
[29] *Medical & Surgical History...Russia* 2:255-6.
[30] *Report of the Committee for scientific enquiries in relation to the cholera epidemics of 1854*. Presented to both Houses of Parliament. London 1855. Dr Thompson's and Dr. Hassall's evidence.
[31] Brunel *Letter Book 12*. p.138. IKB to Benjamin Hawes 5 March 1855. Bristol University Library.
[32] Evans J. *Personal Communication*. 1999.
[33] *Times* 6 Sept 1855.
[34] Soyer A. *Soyer's Culinary Campaign*. 46. London. Routledge, 1857.
[35] Brunel *Letter Book 12*. IKB to Benjamin Hawes, Mar 5 1855. Bristol University Library.
[36] Clapham J. (Ed). *John Brunton's Book*. Cambridge: Cambridge University Press, 1939.
[37] *The Proceedings of the Sanitary Commission dispatched to the seat of War in the East 1855-56*. Presented to both Houses of Parliament. London 1857.
[38] Shepherd J. *Crimean War Doctors*. 1.270-274 Liverpool: Liverpool University Press 1991.
[39] *Medical Times and Gazette* 1855 10:466 and TNA WO 43/991.
[40] Parkes EA. *Report...Renkioi Hospital*.
[41] Brunel I. *The life of Isambard Kingdom Brunel*. 468. London: Longmans Green, 1870.
[42] Parkes EA. *Report...Renkioi Hospital*.
[43] Buzzard T. *With the Turkish Army in the Crimea and Asia Minor*. 303. London: John Murray, 1915.
[44] Hall J. *Observations on the Report of the Sanitary Commissioners in the Crimea during the year 1855 and 1856* by Sir John Hall M.D. K.C.B. Inspector General of Hospitals. 41. London: W Clowes, no date.
[45] Brunel *Letter Book 12*. IKB to John Brunton, 21 May 1955. Bristol University Library.

Chapter 5

Building the Wooden Hospital at Renkioi

'The sound of the hammer in all directions'
Times, 25 December 1855

When the ships laden with the prefabricated components of the new hospital arrived in the Dardanelles and stood off shore, waiting to discharge their cargo into lighters, they were standing in one of the great waterways of the world, well known to sailors and close to one of the quarantine stations which were established by the Turks to prevent the spread of plague and other diseases. Ships arriving from infected ports were regularly stopped there.

Ashore, the countryside near Renkioi was not unfamiliar to British residents living in Constantinople and to travellers with classical interests who included Troy in their itineraries. At home, accounts of life in Turkey had been appearing in the press ever since the war had started. As well as newspaper accounts there were personal impressions of visitors who had meantime returned to Britain; some had come as onlookers to witness the fighting in the last war to be regarded as a social event. The Turks, on the whole, were not thought of very favourably by those going ashore. There was a general belief that corruption was rife, and visitors confirmed that the Turks were dirty and usually living in conditions of great poverty. Gallipoli (now Gelibolu), on the European side of the Narrows, where the allied forces had first landed soon after the outbreak of the war, was known to be a wretched collection of hovels with about 10,000 inhabitants. Often held in higher regard individually, some spoke well of the personal qualities of the Turks. A traveller in Turkey in 1854 stressed the honesty of the Turks, their patriotism and their voluntary contributions to the war effort, while decrying the universal corruption so that 'every official has to look forward to – not what he deserves but what he can get'. This observer believed that it was the Greek inhabitants who were responsible for much of the crime that took place.[1] Renkioi was in an area with a large Greek population.

On the Asiatic side of the Dardanelles, some five miles (8 km) north of Renkioi, lay the polyglot town of Dardanelles (Canakkale) with Turkish, Greek, Armenian, Jewish, and European residents, including a small British community. Very prominent in this was Frederick Calvert, the British Consul. Having helped in the selection of the hospital site, he was to be the intermediary between the Turkish authorities and Parkes and Brunton, and with his brother Frank, a crucial source of information to the hospital staff.

Frederick Calvert was a member of a locally prominent British family which had settled in the Near East. There, the six Calvert brothers during the middle years of the century all became consuls. Representing British interests and power, and exciting respect and sometimes fear in the local inhabitants, Frederick Calvert was a prominent and important figure. He was both a diplomat and a business man and could also be described as an entrepreneur. He had come to the Dardanelles from Malta and was appointed British Consul at the Dardanelles in 1847. As Consul, he was paid a modest salary but allowed to pursue commercial interests, and was considered by a British trader from Smyrna more important than the local Pasha.[2] Turkey was divided into administrative districts with the local pasha at the head, responsible for law and order and taxation. At Dardanelles, the pasha, on good terms with Calvert, was known as 'the pasha with three tails', i.e. of the most important rank, and was an exceedingly wealthy landowner with vast estates; he was both civil and military governor of the province. This pasha had never visited Europe, but he had written two books, one on the immortality of the soul, and the other on the future of Turkey. On one occasion, as wealth and land seemed to be passing into the hands of Christians, another pasha suggested to Frederick Calvert that there would soon be Christian pashas![3] Dardanelles, the seat of local government, was, relative to Europe, a frontier town of the Ottoman Empire and a post in the 'cordon sanitaire' preventing the introduction of plague.

The wealth of the Calvert family lay with Frederick and he, with his younger brother Frank, owned large tracts of farm land close to the hospital site. He dealt with commodities such as grain, Valonia (derived from the acorn cups of a Levantine oak and used in tanning), cotton, and timber. He also made loans to Turkish business men and was the Lloyds agent. His main residence was a large and handsome house dominating the harbour front and evocative of his family's distant aristocratic connections. There he entertained every passing British traveller of note. He had married into the Abbott family, an important English family living in Smyrna. He spoke Turkish, Italian, and French in addition to his native language.[4] His character has been variously described, according to the differing viewpoints of those who knew him, but it is clear that he was hard-headed, energetic, and successful. With the war came the chance to expand his business interests and to serve the interests of his country.

British troops had originally landed at Gallipoli (Gelibolu) on the northern side of the Dardanelles, on 5 April 1854. Most encamped at Bulair (Bolayr) a little further north. Even before their arrival, Frederick Calvert had arranged to billet 5000 of the 15000 men near the town then known as Dardanelles and now as Çanakkale, on the southern (Asiatic) side, choosing a point close to the Lazaretto or quarantine station at Abydos. The spot chosen by Calvert was thought to be unhealthy because of its proximity to the quarantine station. However, Calvert was considered to have done a good job and was successful in arranging supplies for the troops. He himself did not do so well out of his efforts as he met the cost of the hay that he secured for the horses from his own pocket, and it was years before he was reimbursed.[5] That a British hospital should arrive by sea and be landed some five miles (8 km) to the west of Dardanelles, a year after the start of the war, was something which could never have been forecast. However, by the time the hospital arrived, the Turkish and Greek inhabitants of the area were familiar with British soldiers.

The hospital site had been selected on 3 May 1855, but there was little time to spare for the first ship, S.S. Gertrude, arrived on 7 May. The initial fleet of three steamers and two sailing ships was followed by further shipments, so that, by the time the last of these arrived on December 5th 1855, 11,500 tons of materials and stores had been carried in 23 ships. The cargo space required was1½ to 1¾ tons per bed, and the cost £18 to £22 per bed, when delivered ready for shipment.

Once unloading was complete, it remained for Brunton to put Brunel's plans into action, a task he performed with distinction. While the erection of the hospital was Brunton's affair, its overall direction was that of Parkes and, as early as 5 May, he wrote to Lord Paulet, the Commanding officer at Scutari, suggesting that £1000 should be placed at the disposal of Jenner, the Purveyor, to pay for local supplies such as wooden and earthenware drain pipes, tools which were needed and should have been brought out from England, a boat and hire of boats, and the payment of 400 or 500 Turkish soldiers, at the rate per man of 2d per day. If authorised from Constantinople, the Pasha could supply these. They were to build a road from Erenkioi village to the hospital site, a task to be completed in a fortnight.[6]

Parkes made full use of his powers, and was chided by the War Office who feared extravagance. Questions were asked about the payment of a gratuity of £30 to the master of a vessel which took out the 'Wooden Hospital', a term often used. Store huts which had been erected were approved, but no more were to be built locally and stores were to be obtained, so far as possible, from the Commissariat at Scutari and not by local purchase. A note, possibly by Lord Panmure, in the War Office papers states, 'Dr Parkes is not afflicted with Dr Smith's [Director General of the Army Medical Department] complaint of not knowing how to spend money. Curb him in extravagances and let him do things thro' these depts as they ought to be'.[7] At first, Parkes believed that the hospital would eventually grow to its full size. He sent meticulous accounts of what had been done or was proposed. These included every kind of administrative detail, and we know, for example, that in the month of October, amongst thousands of articles washed at the laundry, 76 night caps were washed for the patients. He set out measures to deal with the winter's cold with the arguments for and against each. He recommended coal from England as fuel rather than timber from the local woods, already depleted by the war. The coal was sent out from England; an inner lining for the huts, proposed by Brunton, was referred to Brunel for a decision.

Brunton initially made a minute survey of the district, determining the water supply and deciding where each hut was to be erected. The huts could be arranged in a single row, or parallel rows or in a circle or square, according to the nature of the site. Brunton chose parallel rows. The first huts, two store houses for the Purveyor, were started on 21 May and complete by the 31st. The first medical officer to arrive was Dr Robertson, and the officers were at first boarded in the village of Erenkioi but soon moved to tents on site.

The workforce which he brought out from England consisted of:

Assistant Engineer. William Eassie jun. son of the hospital's contractor

13 carpenters

one pipelayer

three plumbers

one smith

Amongst these skilled workmen were the foreman of the contractor's company, the foreman of the company making the W.C.s, and two plumbers who had worked on the 'iron house' and who could lay pipes.[8]

Only the British workmen were entrusted with the assembly of the hut frames, and when assembled the huts never showed any significant defects. Brunton was also in charge of 150 men of the Army Works Corps; about one thousand Turkish and Greek workmen were also employed on less skilled work.[9] Greek workmen usually did more skilled work than Turkish. Beddoe in one of only two references to Brunton, describes how Brunton viewed his Greek workmen; Brunton summed up as follows: 'They are mostly drunk on Sunday, and on Monday I don't expect them. Tuesday they may put in a fair amount of work, and Wednesday they are all getting ready for the feast-day on Thursday; and on the feast-day they get so drunk that they are of little use on Friday; and Saturday's a half holiday'.[10] William Eassie, Brunton's assistant, gave a much more considered judgement, derived from experience not wholly confined to Renkioi. He begins uncompromisingly: 'the Turk is too slothful, too particular, and too ignorant. The Jew is too costly, too scarce, and too disputable. The Armenian is too exclusive, too inferior, and too peremptory. The Greek alone is pliant, methodical, and social, desiring to see what he has, and buy what he has not, in an animated liberal and steady way.' He goes on to say that 'Turks do not manage to master any language but their own, and can rarely write, Armenians can parley in Turkish or Italian, while Greeks can manage any language. The only person in the matter of commerce who is fit for it is the Greek.' Of the Greek he observes that, although the scapegoat of the East, he is 'fundamentally a noble fellow'. The holidays of Greeks, Armenians, and Turks all fell on different dates, which made for difficulty, but he was impressed by the devotion of the Muslim Turks who were far more scrupulous in their religious observances than the Christian Greeks.[11] Staff sent out from Britain were not entirely problem-free for when the paymaster deducted income tax from the wages of some of the English carpenters, they went home to Gloucester in disgust.[12]

Brunel had designed a set of buildings which could be extended indefinitely to achieve any desired size of hospital to fit any suitable site. The large site of 270 acres that had been selected did not require extensive clearing, so that the first step was to follow Brunel's instructions about providing the water supply and sanitation before starting any building. After surveying the district, Brunton began by arranging for water to be carried underground some 2½ miles by red earthenware pipes from springs in the hills (Figure 22). The water was collected into a stone reservoir and was then distributed on the hospital site by iron pipes and thence to the individual outlets by lead pipes. The springs were about 800 to 1000 feet above sea level and the reservoir 70 feet above the highest house, which itself was 60 feet above sea-level. The reservoir held 50,000 gallons of water. 30 gallons of water could be supplied per patient per day. Square sectioned sewage ducts were dug and lined with tarred oak which Parkes reckoned should be satisfactory for two or three years.[13] The sewerage was flushed by the large quantity of water used daily. Sewage was carried out into the sea for some distance. Both water supply and drainage proved entirely satisfactory. To first lay the water and drainage system had obvious advantages; there had been a precedent at the new town of Birkenhead where this was done in advance of house building. Birkenhead may have been particularly known to Brunel for Paxton laid out Birkenhead Park in 1847; this was later to be the model for Central Park, New York.

The site at Renkioi had been very carefully chosen; repeated elsewhere the siting might not have been so fortunate. At Renkioi, the hospital parts had simply to be unloaded from lighters and carried across virtually flat land on which they could be immediately erected. Had 11,500 tons of material had to be transported across hilly ground to a point inland, a railway would have been necessary, the whole a much more onerous proposition.

Figure 7 shows the layout of Renkioi Hospital as it would have been, had it been completed, with 60 numbered huts accommodating 3000 patients. The hospital huts were arranged at right angles to a central corridor, 22 feet wide. This was covered to reduce exposure and allowed access to each hut. In the first winter it was boarded on one side to lessen the effect of the wind. The corridor was cool and shady in hot weather and allowed patients to be outside and to take some exercise, whatever the weather.

The distance between huts was usually 27 feet on the south side of the corridor and 94 feet on the north. It was a simple matter to increase the number of beds in an orderly way by lengthening the corridor and building more huts. In accordance with the need for beds, a run of 10 huts with a cookhouse and laundry could form a separate hospital or section of a hospital and the numbers could be increased so that even a giant hospital of 3000 beds on one site could be built. On July 12, the hospital was ready for 300 patients; on August 11th for 500; and on December 4th for 1000. When work was discontinued in March 1856, it was ready for 1500, and Parkes

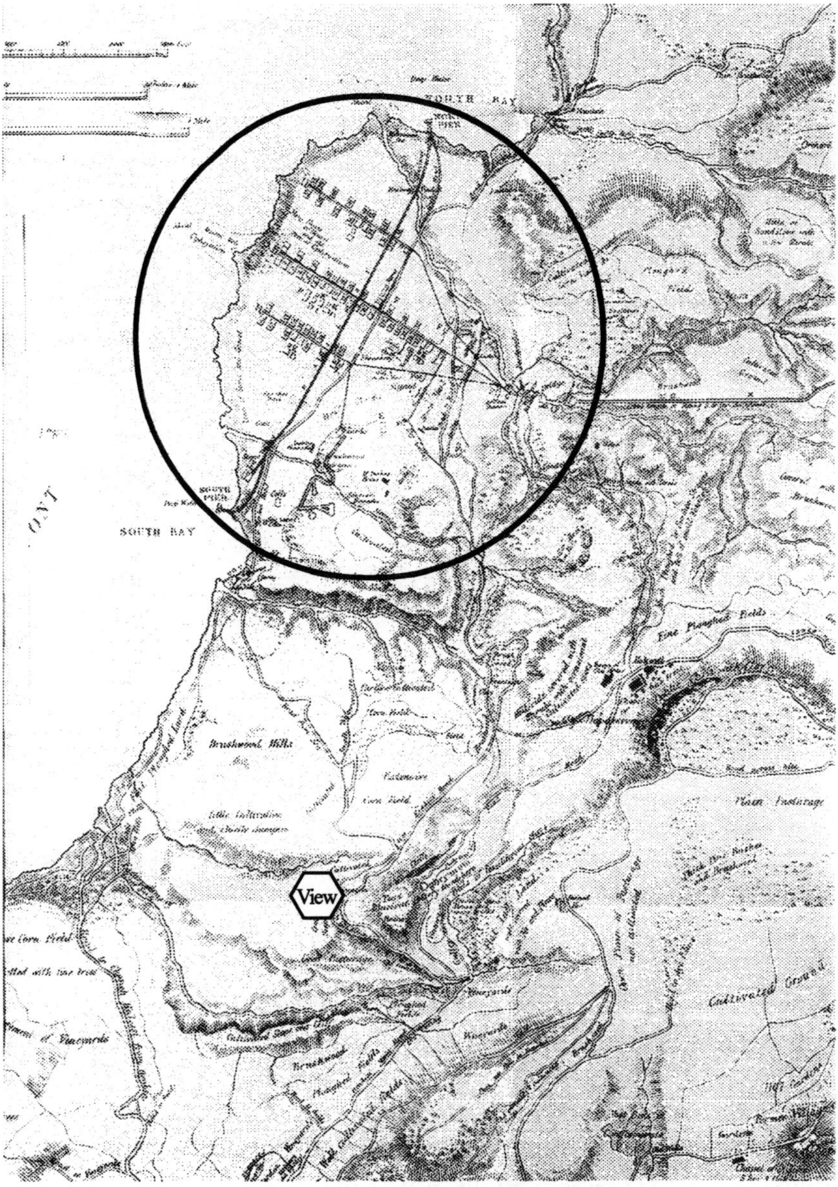

Figure 7: Renkioi Hospital and its Environs.
Also shows viewpoint of complete hospital layout.
Courtesy of the Wellcome Library, London.

believed that in a further three months it would have been ready for the projected total of 3000. However, the two lines of huts parallel to the central spine, each intended to be of 17 huts, were never completed. Parkes writes: 'that one of them to the north was nearly completed when the declaration of peace put a stop to the work'. Assembly of the framework by British tradesmen took some skill, and the work much longer than expected. Dr Sutherland, from the Sanitary Commission, visiting in December 1855, speaks of the huts forming three lanes, so the southern line must have also been started.[14]

Figure 8: The hospital in 1855.
Photograph by Dr Kirk.
By permission of the owner and courtesy of the Scottish National Portrait Gallery.

The plan of an individual hut is shown in Figure 9. Each hut (with 50 beds and measuring 100 feet long, 40 feet wide, and 25 feet high), constituted a ward with a low central partition.

Beds, three feet apart, were arranged in four rows at right angles to this partition along the sides of the ward, while at one end of the ward were the doctor's office, orderlies' room and bathroom, and, at the other, a room with urinals, water closets and washing basins.

Although much larger than the huts sent to the Crimea, the Renkioi huts were not very lofty and in a hot climate could have been very uncomfortable. This Brunel sought to avoid. The windows were sited high which allowed good cross ventilation and there were openings in the gables. He devised an ingenious system of ventilation whereby 1000 to 1500 cubic feet of air per minute was forced into the hut by means of a fan operated by one man supervised by the nearest sentry. Air forced into the hut would be carried by pipes under the floor to escape at regular intervals through

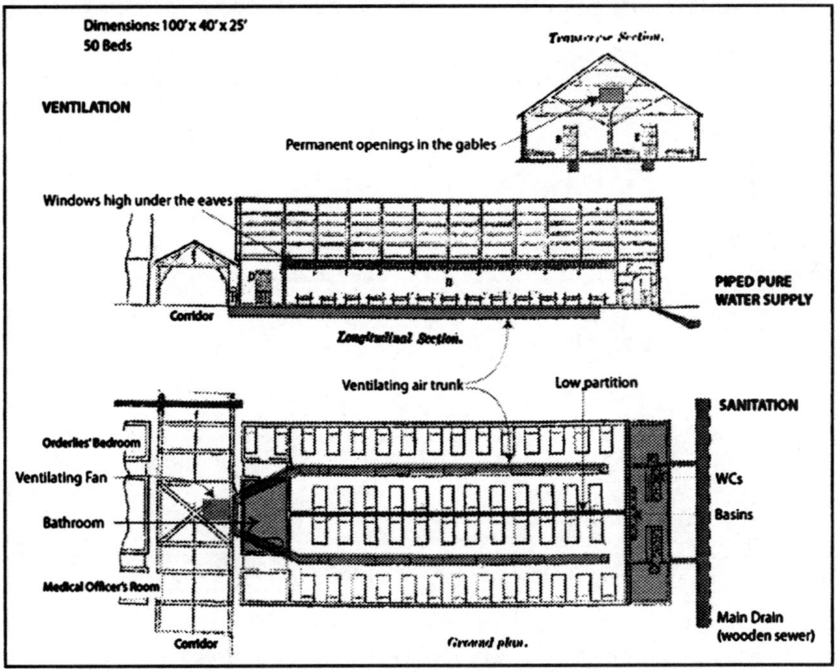

Figure 9: Ward Plan showing ventilation and sanitation systems.
Source: *Brunel. I. The Life of Isambard Kingdom Brunel.*
London: Longmans Green, 1870 (modified).

vents into the ward and then out through narrow opened windows, high in the walls under the eves, or through permanent openings in the gables at the ends of the ward. Expensive in manpower, the fans were never needed as the sea breezes alone ensured that ventilation was sufficient. The swing windows[15] were shaded by the eves and had shutters which could be opened so that glare was avoided. For a proper view of the world the patients must have had to step or be carried outside.

The wood construction was an effective insulation against cold, so that the huts were warm in winter, but in summer, Brunel sought to reduce heat within the ward by ensheathing the hut roofs in tin. This was unsatisfactory for rain seeped in between tin and wood and the tin rusted. Parkes found that the temperature reduction achieved by the tin covering was trivial, only 2 degrees, so that later the tin was stripped from the roofs. Less ambitiously, Brunel arranged that the inside walls of each hut should be lime-washed, slightly tinted so as to avoid glare, and the external walls lime-washed white to decrease the absorption of heat.

Figure 10: Ward interior 1855.
By permission of Liverpool University Press.

As the huts were wooden, heating of the huts was restricted to candles which Brunel believed would be safe, and cleaner than oil. The wards were lit by candles in specially constructed lamps and lanterns, and a small boiler in each ward, heated by candles, provided hot water. In view of fire hazards, the cookhouses and laundries were prefabricated iron buildings. As a precaution, fire engines were sent out from Britain in the stores.

Running water was used to supply the wash basins which were provided with taps, and to flush the water closets and urinals. Brunel was determined to see that the water closets were properly used, even though many of the patients would never have seen one before. In his letter to Dr Parkes, when the whole project was at an early stage, he said he was sending instructions to be pinned on the wall to ensure proper usage, together with supplies of suitable toilet paper.[16] He believed that the recipients would be astonished by this but he knew the difficulties experienced elsewhere.

Portable baths were also provided into which the more helpless patients could be lowered from the bed on a frame or sack. These could be moved anywhere and saved space.

Figure 11: Cookhouse 1855.
Private collection. Courtesy of the Florence Nightingale Library.

Some huts were used for dispensaries and purveyor's stores. To the south of each division of ten huts was placed an iron kitchen where 500 diets could be provided. At the landward end of the main corridor were two iron laundries from which some 4000 gallons of water were passed daily into the sewers. Beyond the laundries, on either side of the ward huts, were the quarters of the doctors and other officers. Looking down the lines of huts they were able to keep some sort of surveillance over the patients. Quarters for them and their wives were completed at an early stage.[17] Brunton at first slept in a tent but later had quarters close to the south quay. Close by were store houses, and elsewhere the nurses' quarters, quarters for the detachment of soldiers attached to the hospital, and various other buildings such as the shambles (slaughter house) and mortuary. The mortuary appeared on the hospital plan as a separate building, well away from others, but no building was specifically marked 'operating theatre'.[18] Operations may have taken place in a ward or a ward allocated for the purpose, rather than in all surgical wards. Each ward possessed a medical officer's room measuring 9½ feet by 7½ feet which, though small, perhaps could have been used for this purpose. At some time a cemetery was constructed. There was some demur when not one but two quays were proposed, but reference was made to Brunel who insisted on two, so that disembarkation would be easy whatever the direction of the wind, almost always north-east or south-west.[19] The railway, shown on the map running over a small viaduct, was soon in operation and ran to the centre, but it too was never completed and never reached the north quay as intended. The original plan envisaged sidings, running along the corridors past the door of each hut, but these were never built. The trolleys were moved by horses, not steam power.

Building began at the start of summer, avoiding the hazards of the winter mud, and continued, with the accompanying noise, throughout the winter of 1855. As early as 21 May 1855, it was said that a photograph and drawings could be sent to the War Office to show the progress made. Some buildings, in the course of construction, are visible in the photographs taken by Kirk and Robertson; most of these photographs were taken before October 1855. It has been suggested that some were sent to Brunel.[20] The huts, made at the High Orchard works, Gloucester, by Eassie's father's firm were carefully erected and never gave trouble, unlike huts in the Crimea which were criticised for poor workmanship, leaving their occupants exposed to the weather, though it was sometimes argued that the ventilation resulting was an advantage.

Brunel's and Florence Nightingale's views about hospital design had a remarkable similarity. Brunel had taken note of the recent outcry about ventilation, and provided at Renkioi many of the features of hospital design which Florence Nightingale subsequently advocated.[21] There is no indication that they ever met. They had medical friends or acquaintances in common such as Sir James Clark who was in close touch with Parkes throughout the project[22] and a great friend of Florence Nightingale and her family. Brunel's huts were larger than the wards that she proposed, but were otherwise very similar. Florence Nightingale preferred a narrower ward with two rows of beds not four, but in only minor respects did Renkioi fall short of the specification that she advocated. Ventilation was acceptable, but the water closets were not in a separate building nor cut off by a lobby from the ward, and their basins were conical, and not hemispherical, as she advised.

Brunel was only officially informed of the Renkioi project two months after Florence Nightingale sailed for Scutari, and though her views were becoming more widely known in 1858, the first edition of her book, *Notes on Hospitals*, was not published until 1859, so that it is unlikely that he could have been aware of her opinions. *Notes* contained references to Renkioi.[23] Colonel Lefroy, later one of Florence Nightingale's immediate circle of advisers, met her for the first time in December 1855 and reported to her after visiting Renkioi.[24] At some time after October 1855, five huts were moved from Renkioi to Scutari[25] so that Florence Nightingale had the opportunity of seeing for herself 'those magnificent huts'.[26] Brunel's first consideration was the comfort of the patients; Florence Nightingale attributed the dismal outcome of hospital admission to overcrowding, lack of space per bed and deficiency of light and ventilation. Providing the former or correcting the latter led them along the same path. Perhaps Florence Nightingale felt that her views were confirmed by what she knew of Renkioi.

[1] Smyth WW. *A Year with the Turks*. 276. West Strand: JW Parker, 1854.
[2] Allen SH. *Finding the walls of Troy*. 86. Berkeley: University of California Press, 1999.
[3] Lefroy Lady. *Autobiography of General Sir John Henry Lefroy*. 155. Private Circulation.
[4] Allen SH. *Finding the Walls of Troy*. 17. Berkeley: University of California Press, 1999.
[5] Allen SH. *Finding the Walls of Troy*. 88. Berkeley: University of California Press, 1999.
[6] TNA. WO 43/991.
[7] TNA. WO 43/991.

[8] Rolt LTC. *Isambard Kingdom Brunel*. 295-6. Harmondsworth: Penguin Books, 1970. The iron house may have been that sent out to the Crimea by the Times for Russell Howard's use.
[9] Brunton, inclined to exaggerate figures, gave a figure of 3000 workmen. On other evidence 1000 appears likely.
[10] Beddoe J. *Memories of Eighty Years*. 72. Bristol: Arrowsmith, 1910.
[11] Rattlebrain (William Eassie). *Romaic Beauties and Trojan Humbugs*. 85. London: Tweedie, 1858.
[12] Beddoe J. *Memories of Eighty Years*. 70. Bristol: Arrowsmith, 1910.
[13] Parkes EA. *Manual of Practical Hygiene*. 600. London: Churchill, 1864.
[14] *The Proceedings of the Sanitary Commission dispatched to the Seat of War in the East 1855-56*. Viii. 1857.
[15] *The Proceedings of the Sanitary Commission dispatched to the Seat of War in the East 1855-56*. 59. 1857.
[16] Brunel *Letter Book 12*. IKB to Dr. Parkes, 13 Apr 55. Bristol University Library.
[17] Clapham J. (Ed). *John Brunton's Book*. 60. Cambridge: Cambridge University Press, 1939.
[18] The third (expanded and revised) edition of Florence Nightingale's *Notes on Hospitals*, contains Florence Nightingale's views about operating theatres but does not show an operating theatre on a plan of Netley hospital, the large military hospital built near Southampton immediately after the war. Perhaps the operating theatre was thought of as a room, well lit from the north by daylight, not an elaborately equipped hospital feature as now.
[19] TNA. WO 43/991.
[20] Lawson J. *Dr John Kirk and Dr William Robertson: Photographers in the Crimea. History of Photography 1988*; 12:227-241.
[21] Nightingale F. *Notes on hospitals* 3rd Ed. London: Longman Green, 1863.
[22] Jenner W. *Observations on the work and character of the late E.A. Parkes MD, F.R.S. British Medical Journal* 1876; 2:33-34. Sir James Clark was responsible for Parkes' appointment as Superintendent.
[23] A table and the following quotation: 'The only hospital in which this arrangement of four rows of beds could be comparatively unobjectionable would be in a one-storied hut hospital, ventilated through the ceiling, like that of Dr. Parkes at Renkioi.* But his were magnificent huts, and the partition was little more than a bulkhead.'
[24] Lefroy Lady. *Autobiography of General Sir Henry Lefroy*. 160. Privately printed.
[25] Parkes EA. *Report...Renkioi Hospital*. 13.
[26] Nightingale F. *Notes on Hospitals*. 14. London: Parker, 1859.

Chapter 6

A Model Hospital

> One figure appeared ubiquitous – namely that of the Superintendent, Dr Parkes
>
> *The Times, 20 October 1865, describing the first disembarkation of patients*

Renkioi Hospital was described by a good judge as 'in many respects a model hospital'.[1] The single most important person at Renkioi was the Medical Superintendent, Dr Edmund Parkes, a remarkably gifted physician. By then he was 36 years of age with the advantage of some previous military experience. On him depended the smooth running of the whole Hospital. If Brunel was the great personality of the first half of this story then Parkes, though more restrained, was that of the second.

Edmund Parkes was born in 1819, the son of William Parkes and Frances, daughter of Thomas Byers, nephew and partner of Josiah Wedgwood.[2] He qualified at University College Hospital in London in 1840. He was an exceptional student and, as a student, began investigative work with, as his mentor, his uncle, Anthony Todd Thomson, Professor of Materia Medica and Medical Jurisprudence and an expert on botany. Now he became familiar with chemical manipulations. Later, on Thomson's death, he completed and edited Thomson's *A Practical Treatise on Diseases of the Skin*. Parkes then served in the army from 1842-1845 as Assistant Surgeon to the 84th Regiment of Foot, at first in Burma at Moulmein and then, for the greater part of his service, in India near Madras. His regiment was engaged on garrison duties and he became experienced in the prevalent Indian afflictions, diarrhoeal diseases and cholera, and hepatitis. Already interested in research, he studied the illnesses afflicting prisoners in a large civil prison. Parkes reveals himself in an account of cholera which he wrote while in India.[3] He set out to examine the features of cholera and carried out 47 post-mortem examinations, all under hot and exacting conditions without, of course, any refrigeration. The examinations were performed soon after death and recorded meticulously. Of particular interest is his account of a treatment that had a logical basis but was fortunately abandoned in its original form. In the 1830s, a method of treating cholera had been introduced where fluid (saline, salt solution) was injected intravenously.[4] This produced an almost immediate improvement, due to the replacement of fluid lost through diarrhoea. Unfortunately improvement was very short-lived and it was realised that mortality with this treatment was even higher than without.

Parkes modified the treatment, suggesting that, in cholera, there was loss of tissue which might be reconstituted by giving the patient albumen intravenously. His experience told him which of his patients were likely to die and he was able to make some prediction of the number of hours a stricken patient would survive. After trying saline alone, over the course of months he selected five patients for whom he held out no hope of recovery. Modifying the original treatment, he injected intravenously into each, from 4½ to 11 pints (in two infusions) of an alkaline salt solution (containing sesqui carbonate of soda 4 drachms, chloride of soda 2 drachms), to which he added the albumen of one or two eggs. Two of the patients suffered rigors (sudden shivering, then fever) which he would not have expected at this stage of the illness and which he put down to treatment. All improved temporarily due to rehydration but all died, one, three days after treatment, but the remainder after only a few hours, very much as he would have expected had they not received this treatment.[5] The likelihood of infection and of the danger of using a solution not in physical balance with the patient's blood, a reaction to albumen (probably the cause of the rigors), embolism or blockage of a blood vessel by a solid fragment or by accidentally administered air, and the strain of the very rapid infusion at an uncertain temperature all militated against success. However, he set out the most important principle of modern treatment: 'The object of the injection is not to cure Cholera but to restore and to sustain the circulation for some hours, until the healing force of nature may repair the lesions of the blood and restore to the vitiated fluid its normal composition'.[6] Though the proposal was not sufficiently refined, the whole enterprise shows him as a determined, careful, innovative physician working under difficult conditions; and moreover brave.

Figure 12: Dr. Edmund Parkes.
With permission of the Library and Archives Service,
London School of Hygiene & Tropical Medicine.

Parkes' scientific curiosity had been fruitful, and on return to England he obtained his M.D. with a thesis on dysentery and hepatitis in India. At the age of 30 he was appointed Professor of Clinical Medicine and Physician at University College Hospital. Recognised as an able teacher, he was popular with students. He put his arguments very clearly, and many of his lectures were published and are exemplary accounts. From 1852 to 1855, he was Editor of the *British and Foreign Medical Review*. Parkes was always able to add worthwhile comment, and many of his reviews were, 'in reality original articles and were composed with as much care as if I was about to affix my name to them'.[7] When William Jenner, then in his twenties, submitted a paper to the *Edinburgh Medical Journal*, Parkes gave this advice; 'If you place the conclusions first, whoever is interested in the subject will read them carefully, and then will read what follows to see how you prove the points that interest him'.[8] Just before he arrived at Renkioi, he delivered an authoritative review of fever, in which he agreed with the conclusions of Virchow, the great German pathologist (who later was to visit Troy), that fever was an elevation, controlled by the nervous system, of normal body temperature due to increased tissue change.[9]

Photographs of Parkes show a tall rather thin man with moustache and sideburns and a calm expression; they do not give any hint of his extraordinary sweetness of character, and of his uncertain health. John Beddoe, then an Assistant Surgeon serving under Parkes wrote of him years later, as having 'every virtue under heaven', a very warm endorsement from someone in close contact with him under sometimes trying conditions.[10] The good opinion of Parkes as a man was echoed by everyone who knew him, an opinion summarised by Sir John Simon, the great sanitary reformer, twenty years after he died. He wrote, 'it seemed that wherever he worked, his public spirit, and the kindliness and bright sincerity of his nature, won the confidence and affection of his fellow-workers... His life... an arduous gallant struggle against... ill-health'.[11]

Parkes married in 1850, his bride being Mary Jane Chattock of Solihull, where Parkes himself spent part of his childhood. She was with him at Renkioi. They had no children. There was one cloud on the horizon. In 1851, soon after taking up his duties as Professor, he had leave of absence of some months duration, on account of illness. The recommendation was signed by Sir James Clark, Dr Walshe, Professor of Medicine, whose previous position Parkes had taken, Dr Jenner who was appointed Assistant Physician on Parkes' promotion, and Mr Quain, the celebrated anatomist and surgeon.[12] His illness is likely to have been tuberculosis which was to be responsible for later ill health and eventually his death. This was one explanation as to why he never had any large private practice. Despite this, he was always known as a prodigious worker.

In his Report, Parkes described every important aspect of the hospital. He found himself in charge of a staff of about 120, including the medical staff. The medical staff usually numbered about 20 at any one time. Forty was the average age of the senior doctors, and 26 that of the juniors, who were classed as Assistant Physicians or Surgeons.[13] The medical men were able and at an early stage of their careers. The senior doctors included Spencer Wells (Senior Surgeon and previously at Smyrna) and Holmes Coote, both Divisional Surgeons, and Henry Goodeve (Senior Physician) and William Robertson, both Divisional Physicians. Spencer Wells was a year older than Parkes, had had a career in the navy, and like Parkes, had been editor of a medical journal, in this case the *Medical Times and Gazette*; he was to become President of the Royal College of Surgeons of England. With the closure of the civil hospital at Smyrna in October 1855, he had moved from there to Renkioi. Holmes Coote had had a promising early career as a Surgeon at St Bartholomew's Hospital. Henry Goodeve, then aged 48 and the oldest doctor, was a physician with great experience in India where he had occupied the post of Inspector of Civil Hospitals. He had 'an open cheery countenance to which the effects of his wound gave a singularly martial air'.[14] The wound had been a gunshot wound, injuring the facial nerve with paralysis of one side of the face, sustained while he was stationed at Rampour and was hunting tigers in the jungle. Throughout his life he was known for his public spirit, and by the time he was at Renkioi he had initiated a scheme for giving the benefits of English education to high caste and other Hindus. He had brought from India four young Brahmins, placed them at University College, and superintended their careers. William Robertson, whose maternal uncle was General Sir George Brown, had been Physician to Edinburgh Royal Infirmary. He was an able physician, interested in mathematics and medical statistics, but a shy, retiring, and unobtrusive manner (the opposite of his uncle), meant that he did not go quite so far as might have been expected.[15]

The junior doctors still had their lives and careers ahead, and nearly half had had their initial training in Scotland (Appendix 3). They included John Kirk, who was soon to accompany Livingstone on his second Zambesi expedition; when appointed to that expedition he was described as accomplished botanist, zoologist, and physiologist. John Beddoe was married to the niece of Professor Robert Christison of Edinburgh, whose son, David Christison, was among the Renkioi staff. Beddoe's subject was to be ethnology; we know, as a consequence, that when he qualified his height was 5ft. 8½ inches. He had a fair complexion, rather bright wavy brown hair, a yellow beard and blue eyes; a head rather large and lofty and of medium breadth, but the base small in proportion. He was ambidexter (sic) and known to the Turks as Sarisakal Hekim, Dr Yellowbeard.[16] Few more complete accounts of the physical appearance of a newly qualified doctor must exist. While a student, he had given first aid to Joseph Lister, injured when both a stone and Beddoe, had fallen on him when they were rock climbing at Salisbury Crags, Edinburgh.[17] Lister had had to be removed, bruised, on a stretcher. No doctors died while serving at Renkioi but one, Dr Holland, who suffered from epilepsy, died a few days after returning to England.[18]

Medical staff had come to Renkioi anxious to learn. At Renkioi, there were two exceptionally good teachers, Edmund Parkes himself and Spencer Wells, the Senior Surgeon. Wells was to become a pioneer in abdominal surgery and began to remove the diseased ovary with success, even before Lister's discoveries made abdominal surgery practicable instead of unacceptably dangerous. Of the doctors who worked at Renkioi, three became Fellows of the Royal Society, three professors in British medical schools while Sir John Kirk, a doctor and botanist, had a distinguished career as a diplomat and administrator, playing a large part in the abolition of the slave trade in Zanzibar. Robertson became statistician to the Scottish office; Thomas Rhodes Armitage, who became blind himself not very long after the war, went on to be a pioneer in the care of the blind and a leading exponent of Braille.[19] Carl (later Charles) Bader became a distinguished ophthalmologist;[20] Christison, who was said to have left Renkioi in ill-health, turned from medicine to become one of the pioneers of scientific archaeology in Scotland.[21] Others held responsible posts, and the careers of all who can be traced have been recorded.[22] The medical staff fulfilled their early promise and no doubt, despite the fewness of admissions, owed something to Renkioi in the process.

The medical staff visited the wards at 9.30 am and again in the evening. The orderly officer was obliged to go round twice at night. Holmes Coote, writing long afterwards, remarked on the long distance to be covered, perhaps a quarter of a mile, so that extra labour was needed to convey food and necessities.[23] Parkes' own Report submitted to the Secretary of State for War is the only comprehensive account of how the hospital dealt with its patients. This drew on the excellent reports from the medical and surgical divisions of the hospital which were submitted to Parkes each month[24] and which now give us a very good idea of medical practice at Renkioi. Parkes, as Superintendent, required a special report if anything went wrong, much better Parkes believed, than the military routine of a report to the orderly officer.[25] The duties of the doctors, nurses, and orderlies were displayed in each ward. Printed sick returns and other forms were used as in military hospitals. The medical condition of the patient must have been recorded in the personal notes of the attending doctor. At the civil hospital at Smyrna, such notes are referred to.[26] The official records at Renkioi were the bed tickets hanging on the patient's bed which gave the patient's whole treatment including diet.[27] The arrangement allowed the patient to see his bed ticket and know what had been ordered ('if he did not get it he was sure to complain'), but the meal ordinarily had to be ordered the day before, something which Florence Nightingale sought to avoid. At the London Hospital, there were no case notes combining administrative and medical information until the 1890s.[28]

The nursing staff (Appendix 3) initially consisted of 20 paid nurses and five 'lady' nurses, one of whom, Mrs Newman, was the Superintendent. Ultimately some 35 names appeared on the list of nurses employed at Renkioi. Apart from Mrs Newman, of the other lady nurses, two had additional administrative duties and two purely nursing duties, one of whom was Miss Parkes, sister of Dr Parkes. The nurses were paid and were of varying quality. Florence Nightingale had responsibility for all nurses in the East but played no part in their selection or management at Renkioi. This overall responsibility was her only connection with Renkioi. Nurses were selected by Dr Parkes and Sir James Clark.

By this stage of the war, six months after Florence Nightingale had landed at Scutari with her nurses, doubts about female nurses were becoming fewer. Bransby Roberts, an Assistant Civil Surgeon, could only say of the lady nurses at Renkioi, 'The Lady Nurses is (sic) rather a farce here as there have only been 5 and the chief thing they have to do is to look after the wine etc and prevent the nurses drinking it... I look upon them as a failure for any practical use beside looking after the stock of clothes, wine etc in the ward – call them storekeepers and it would come nearer the mark'. [29]

Parkes thought otherwise and said that 'the nursing of the soldiers could not have been better in any other hospital in the country'. It is likely that Parkes and Florence Nightingale met when Parkes was in Constantinople and her biographer states that, 'there is voluminous correspondence among her papers showing that she was constantly consulted upon the site and arrangements of these hospitals [i.e. Smyrna and Renkioi]. The Medical Superintendent of the hospital at Renkioi was Dr E.A. Parkes with whom Miss Nightingale formed a friendship which endured to the end of his life'.[30]

The hospital orderlies (Appendix 3) fell into three categories, civilians, soldiers sent from Chatham and unavailable for other than hospital service, and soldiers belonging to the regiments in the Crimea who, arriving as patients, had then volunteered for service at the hospital. From this heterogeneous group, a very good staff was assembled. The civil orderlies had been well chosen and were most respectable and trustworthy. Among the soldiers were some very good men. In three or four instances men were found who had a remarkable aptitude for nursing and took pleasure in it; they possessed all the feminine sympathy, kindness, and consideration, and were as much liked by the patients as the nurses. However generally attentive and kind, they were more usually adapted to the rough work of the wards. They undertook all the non-nursing duties. From them a certain number were selected as ward masters and assistant stewards with a small increase in pay; they could be demoted if unsatisfactory.

Other staff consisted of the Steward, Apothecary, four Dispensers and one orderly dispenser, Head Cook, Cook, and Assistant Cook, Head Baker and three Assistant Bakers, Upper Laundress, with an orderly acting as assistant laundress, Clinical Clerk, Secretary to the Superintendent, two men from the Army Works Corps, an artisan, and orderlies with specific non-nursing duties such as storekeeper.

Parkes always spoke well of all his staff. Mr Hooper, the Laundry Superintendent, he singled out for introducing a van laundry, capable of being drawn by one horse, containing boiler, washing-machine, and drying closet, which, with one laundry wagon for every 500 beds, would be valuable for any hospital on the move.[31]

There were still others on the staff including John Brunton, engineer, William Eassie, assistant engineer and son of the contractor, and 18 workmen, together with the Purveyor, Jenner[32] and a succession of army officers. These were Lieutenant Bennett, Major Chads, Captain Bazalgette and Captain La Touche who were in charge of a guard of 30 soldiers; they also had various other military duties, including some at Abydos, then a convalescent hospital and subsequently barracks.

Parkes had ultimate responsibility for the whole staff and proved himself an able organiser, in charge of an enormous hospital with a potential capacity of 3000 beds. In fact, the largest number of patients at any one time was 642, and building ceased when 1500 beds were open. All accounts indicate that Parkes administered the hospital in an exemplary manner. An internal War Office minute in 1856 stated that, 'I have no doubt that up to the last it [i.e. the hospital] will maintain its extremely high level of efficiency – never having had a complaint or failure since it first started'. [33]

Parkes never seems to have experienced serious disciplinary problems for there is only a mention of one orderly, after a bout of drunkenness, being dismissed and found work at lower pay in Brunton's workforce. Misbehaving patients were reported to their commanding officer on discharge. The doctors, though civilians, had no problems with discipline among their patients or the staff. At Renkioi, with no town very close, drunkenness does not seem to have been a problem, but the death of Sergeant Powell, 'reputed to be one of the finest men in the British army' and convalescent from an acute infection, was ascribed to drunkenness and exposure,[34] though his death does not appear to have been recorded under these headings. He had been drinking in the village of Erenkioi but, after a chilly night, was found next morning lying by the road. Everywhere, drunkenness was a scourge and at Smyrna and Scutari, it was not unusual for soldiers to be seen, lying in the road, dead drunk.

Parkes' Report on Renkioi Hospital is comprehensive, with the reasons for every decision given. He could oversee every hospital activity. He organised medical and surgical divisions, each of 10 wards of 50 beds each. The divisions were in charge of a Senior Physician (Henry Goodeve) and a Senior Surgeon (Spencer Wells) respectively. They were responsible to the Medical Superintendent whose duties were mainly administrative. The wards, each occupying a single hut and classified as medical or surgical, were in charge of an Assistant Physician or Surgeon responsible for medical work and hygiene. Apart from a request from Spencer Wells for better beds for surgical patients, there were no complaints about the hospital equipment.[35]

In each division, a lady nurse superintended the paid nurses and, as initially there were 20 paid nurses, Parkes could place two nurses in each ward. As the number of wards grew this was reduced to one nurse per ward. Parkes appointed a ward master in charge of 40 orderlies. One nurse and four orderlies in each ward gave the same staff ratio, of one attendant to ten patients, as that of a military hospital.

Just as medical work was organised by divisions, so were supporting services. Each division had its own kitchen and the Purveyor was in overall charge of an office and stores which served each of them and drew from a central store near the landing pier. The same was true of other services and there was, for instance, on each ward, a linen cupboard which always had an extra supply of linen for emergencies, and was supplied from a divisional store. The divisions were complete in themselves and self-supporting, and the hospital could be extended by creating further divisions.

As a civil hospital, Renkioi differed from military hospitals in important ways. Parkes had the responsibilities of both the combatant officer in command of an ordinary military hospital, and of the senior medical officer. As Superintendent, the whole responsibility for the hospital devolved upon him; his earliest instructions from the War Office stated that he 'was wholly responsible for the efficiency of the hospital'.[36] This situation was quite different from the military hospital where the senior medical officer was powerless about arrangements which were not purely medical. Relations were very good between Parkes and Brunton, the Engineer, and Jenner, the Purveyor. Besides being Engineer, Brunton in his relationship to the Turkish authorities and local inhabitants, was a kind of land agent for the hospital estate, though Parkes was finally responsible. Thus Parkes had an effective interest in every aspect of the hospital.

The position of the junior doctors was also different from that in a military hospital. In a military base hospital, the senior posts were administrative[37] and the running of the hospital was dependent on once or twice-weekly inspections by these higher ranking medical officers. On the wards they interfered with the clinical work of their juniors, though long out of practice. At Renkioi the arrangement was that of a civil hospital with the junior doctor more directly responsible for his clinical work to his senior. Larger civil hospitals were appointing resident medical officers to assist the visiting physicians and surgeons and, in the largest, other more junior medical staff.

The strength of Brunel's plans, which were meticulously executed, was that they encouraged return to health, and discouraged the spread of infection. Despite the fact that views about infection and the causation of disease (Chapter 2) have changed completely since the Crimean War, Brunel's provisions stand up well to modern scrutiny. Parkes was able to turn them to good account.

Brunel was insistent on a pure water supply. The pure spring water was safe and carried from the hills through pipes to the reservoir. This was covered and away from any source of contamination; the reservoir was never empty, and water was then distributed in a closed and satisfactory system. The wonders of the water supply were a constant source of amazement and delight; the *Times* correspondent wrote of the water, 'when cooled in porous jars it tastes as fresh and pure as at a fountain head, and believe me, in this climate there is really no luxury more highly prized'.[38] Not only did a satisfactory water supply raise standards of personal cleanliness, but it encouraged more hygienic conditions generally.

Brunel's kitchens, with running water supplied, were much better than those in barracks and ensured satisfactory meals. At Renkioi, boiling was not the only method of preparing meat; it could be roasted in the stoves designed by Soyer, 'We could bake and boil but did not steam',[39] a better situation than that described in the statement that 'when a soldier enters the service, he has the prospect of dining on boiled meat every day for 21 years, if he is enabled to serve so long', for only coppers were provided in barracks.[40]

The patients' rations were much the same as at Scutari. The ration was weighed before cooking and the meat sent in a net to each ward for all patients on full diet. Another net was sent for those on half diet. The meat was divided in the ward. The diet scales Parkes proposed for officers and for 'artizans,' appeared 'very liberal' and were sanctioned initially for only two months while the hospital was being erected. The daily allowance for officers comprised many items including 1½ lbs (680g) of bread, 1lb (453g) of meat, and 12oz (340g) of vegetables while for 'artizans' the amounts were 1½ lbs (680g), 1½ lbs (680g) and 1lb (453g) respectively. There can have been no difficulty about supplying fresh vegetables (listed in the botanical appendix to Parkes' Report); nowadays they can be seen, growing in profusion in the district. Medical comforts were shipped to hospitals in the East, and consisted of huge quantities of dried vegetables, preserved meats and soups, preserved milk, tea and sugar, and, most commonly alluded to for treatment, arrowroot (122550 lbs) and alcoholic drinks.[41] At Renkioi, comforts were alluded to and wine was an important adjunct to treatment.

Brunel's grasp of the importance of diarrhoeal disease was amply justified. Brunel not only installed water closets but gave precise instructions for their use. At the London Hospital in December 1818, a House Committee minute records that 'the water closets which tend so much to the cleanliness and comfort of the wards, require frequent and expensive repairs, many of which are rendered necessary by the improper substances, such as tow etc., being used in them.' Patients putting in improper substances, and nurses failing to report defects, were to be dismissed.[42] At the Garrison Hospital, Brompton, Chatham, water closets were closed during the day to prevent their indiscriminate use. The discipline of the hospital and Brunel's instructions avoided all this, and no such difficulties were reported at Renkioi

Bedding was kept in good condition. Parkes was particularly proud of the laundry which was under the charge of a Superintendent from one of the London baths and wash houses, who supervised a corps of Greek washerwomen. Soiled linen was collected daily and exchanged for fresh, while the drying closets with a temperature of 400F sterilised clothing and killed vermin with which blankets, coats and shirts were often swarming. Vermin included lice, carriers of typhus, and heat sterilisation effectively halted the spread of other infections as well.

Renkioi showed itself to be a model hospital with up-to-date views. News of the rarity of spread of disease at Renkioi even reached the pages of the *Times*. 'There has been no epidemic, no spread of disease from bed to bed, and no case of indigenous disease'.[43]

Though these were pre-Listerian days, Spencer Wells, in charge of the Surgical Division, was well aware of the danger of infection and had himself written of how he had noticed fewer patients with pyaemia after their ward had been moved from immediately above a dissecting room; he considered the move had halted the spread of disease.[44] It was well known that wound infections could spread from wound to wound. Faced with sloughing wounds and gross infection, Wells took 'great care that no inoculation of the patients should take place by sponges etc.'[45] Referring to the only patient who died as result of wounds, he describes how the fatal case declared itself the day after admission. The patient suffered from pyaemia following a severe wound of the face. He was carefully isolated until he died, and a post-mortem examination was then conducted; post-mortem examinations were usual at Renkioi. Another patient finally did well who had a granulating wound and developed general symptoms with signs of a sloughing, phagydarma (sic), followed by the loss of much soft tissue but eventual recovery. He had at once been removed from the ward. Wells was an excellent surgeon and unlike Lister who, until late in life, was careless on this point, was insistent on cleanliness. His entry in the *Dictionary of National Biography* states that he worked in absolute silence, took the greatest care in the selection of his instruments, and submitted his assistants to a firm discipline that proved of the highest value to them in after life. At the conclusion of every operation he superintended the cleaning and drying of each instrument, and packed it in its case in the most orderly manner. There is no reason to think that his practice changed substantially between his earlier and later years.

Infection, not just complicating surgery but the whole subject, interested Spencer Wells and soon after the war started he wrote about quarantine for plague and smallpox in Turkey.[46] Such infectious diseases were a concern of the Renkioi doctors, though neither of these two 'zymotic' diseases were seen at Renkioi. However, typhus occurred, an infectious condition spread by lice, detected not only on the bodies but especially on the clothing of the men of the Land Transport and Army Works Corps.[47] One doctor, one nurse, and one orderly contracted typhus, and the orderly died.[48] An Assistant Pack Store Keeper, who was never near any of the sick, was occupied in sorting the filthy packs of the Land Transport Corps and complained greatly of the stench of the clothes. Six days later he sickened with typhus. Drawing on this experience, Parkes advocated that on board ship with typhus about, separating patients with fever from others and packs from their owners should be the rule.[49] Believing typhus very contagious, keen on plenty of air and more space between beds, and unaware of the role of lice, he considered isolation the key to prevention. The laundry arrangements at Renkioi for destroying lice were of course remarkably effective. The infrequency of the staff at Renkioi catching infectious diseases is an indication of the efficacy of the steps taken to prevent this.

Wards were medical or surgical. Cross infection could arise through admitting patients with infected wounds to medical wards or with infectious fevers to surgical wards. There are no indications of this being a problem at Renkioi. Isolation in the bathroom was sometimes necessary if a bed elsewhere was not immediately available.

Such was everyday practice at Renkioi. It is worth examining the somewhat different views of one who was at the very centre of affairs,

Florence Nightingale. Her views about hospital design were compared with those of Brunel in the last chapter. She believed in the miasmatic spread of most infectious diseases, the most commonly held view. That theory was to be disproved by the discovery of bacteria. However, without knowing their cause, from her immense experience, she understood the danger that hospitals presented to their patients and the devastating frequency of infections such as pyaemia and erysipelas acquired in hospital. Allotting patients to separate medical and surgical wards was recent.

Three years after the war, she was asked to advise on the plans for the re-construction of the hospital at Aylesbury by her brother-in-law, Sir Harry Verney. She concluded that, at Aylesbury, there should be separate male medical and surgical wards, and a mixed medical and surgical ward for women, as the number of capital (major) operations for women had been scarcely one in fourteen months. She went on to say:

> Also a hospital would never work, if the Medical Men decidedly objected to mixing of the medical and surgical patients e.g. it would never be right to put amputation and fever cases together should these form the average cases of the hospital. ...As to medical and surgical wards. This is purely a Doctor's point. If they are satisfied so am I. I will venture to say that I could keep a properly constructed ward so safe as to put medical and surgical cases safely together in it. But doctors are generally very strong against this... I had much rather mix surgical and medical cases in two good wards (male and female) than have them unmixed in four bad ones – I have done.[50]

Going too far she wrote elsewhere that, 'With proper sanitary precautions, diseases reputed to be the most "infectious" may be treated in wards among other sick without any dangers'.[51] The last view was Utopian. She had no use for the terms 'contagion' and 'infection' which she thought of as nebulous, opposing her conviction of what could be achieved by proper sanitary arrangements – by which she particularly meant, avoiding overcrowding and ample ventilation and light.[52] She was devoted to the 'pavilion principle' with widely separated hospital buildings and stressed that the post-mortem room and Dead House (mortuary) should be outside the hospital building and that post mortem examination should never be conducted in the operating theatre, a temptation because of the availability of table and instruments.[53] She insisted on absolute cleanliness. Believing primarily in atmospheric spread of disease, emanations and a tainted atmosphere, she considered that hospital sewers could become cesspools of the most dangerous kind for, if not properly ventilated, emanations from them could be blown back through the drain pipes into hospital wards. At Scutari, until the arrival of the Sanitary Commission, the privies consisted merely of a marble slab with an opening communicating with a vertical pipe of red tile carried down into a drain in the basement. Thus for her, even in this instance, the spread of disease was miasmatic.

Because not all her views have stood up to scientific enquiry, some are now hard to understand.[54] [55] Questioned however about to what she ascribed mortality at Scutari, she replied without hesitation, 'To sanitary defects'.[56] The worth of the practical measures she advocated was very great. Her ideas had developed at Scutari in appalling circumstances, the causes of which were unknown to her and everyone else; it was to be more than 20 years before the discovery of bacteria explained them. The truth of Pasteur's dictum (Chapter 2) is clear, but long after he had expressed his views and long after Scutari, she retained her belief in miasmatic spread. But her absolute conviction that spread of disease was preventable has always been an immense contribution.

[1] Lefroy Lady. *Autobiography of General Sir Henry Lefroy*. 147. Privately printed. Colonel, later General, Lefroy was not a doctor but Scientific Adviser to the War Office and friend and adviser to Florence Nightingale.

[2] *Dictionary of National Biography*.

[3] Parkes EA. *Researchers into the Pathology and Treatment of Asiatic or Algide Cholera*. London: John Churchill, 1847.

[4] Latta TA. *Saline venous injections in cases of malignant cholera*. Lancet 1831-2; 2:274-277. Latta later (ibid. 429) indicated that the addition of albumen to the infusion had been contemplated or tried by others.

[5] Parkes EA. *Researches into the Pathology and Treatment of Asiatic or Algide Cholera*. 218-240 London: John Churchill. 1847.

[6] Parkes EA. *Researches into the Pathology and Treatment of Asiatic or Algide Cholera*. 238-239 London: John Churchill, 1847.

[7] Parkes EA. *Letter of application for the post of Professor of Clinical Medicine*, University College London, 26 Jan 1849.
[8] Jenner W. *Lectures and Essays on Fevers and Diphtheria 1849-79*. viii. London: Rivington, Percival & Co., 1893.
[9] Parkes EA. *Gulstonian Lectures, RCP. Medical Times and Gazette* 1855. 11: 253, 279, 331, 472, 535,561.
[10] Beddoe J. *Memories of eighty years*. 62. London: Arrowsmith, 1910.
[11] Simon J. *English Sanitary Institutions*. 2nd Ed. 244. London: Murray, 1897.
[12] Letter 3 Feb 1851 EA Parkes to CC Atkinson. Library, University College, London.
[13] Shepherd J. *The Crimean Doctors*. 2.441. Liverpool: Liverpool University Press, 1991.
[14] Obituary. *Medical Times and Gazette* 1884; 2:65.
[15] Obituary. *Edinburgh Medical Journal* 1882; 28:382-384.
[16] Beddoe J. *Memories of eighty years*. 123. Bristol: Arrowsmith, 1910.
[17] Beddoe J. *Memories of eighty years*. 56. Bristol: Arrowsmith, 1910.
[18] Obituary. *Medical Times & Gazette* 1856. 12.638.
[19] Obituary. *Lancet* 1890; 2:1004.
[20] Collins ET. *The History and Tradition of the Moorfields Eye Hospital*. London: HK Lewis, 1929.
[21] *Times* 24 January 1912.
[22] Shepherd J. *Crimean War Doctors 2*. 440-1. Liverpool: Liverpool University Press. 1991.
[23] Coote H. *Correspondence on 'Hospitalism'. British Medical Journal* 1869; 1.297.
[24] TNA W 43.991.
[25] *Royal Commission...Sick and Wounded* 1858. Q930.
[26] *Royal Commission...Sick and Wounded* 1858. Q1042.
[27] *Royal Commission...Sick and Wounded* 1858. Q936.
[28] Evans J. *Personal Communication*. 1999.
[29] Bransby Roberts. *Letters*.
[30] Cook ET. *The Life of Florence Nightingale*. 1:174. London: Macmillan, 1913.
[31] Parkes EA. *Report...Renkioi Hospital*. 22.
[32] Parkes EA. *Report...Renkioi Hospital*. Mr K Jenner who had been at Alma later served in the Crimea. He was the brother of Dr William Jenner, Parkes' colleague at University College Hospital.
[33] TNA WO 43/991 Public Records Office, Kew.
[34] Beddoe J. *Memories of eighty years*. 106. Bristol: Arrowsmith, 1910.
[35] TNA WO 43/991 Public Records Office, Kew.
[36] TNA WO 43.991 Public Records Office, Kew.
[37] *Royal Commission...Sick and Wounded* 1858. Q10060.
[38] *Times* 6 September 1855. The site of the operating theatre was often omitted from hospital plans.

[39] *Royal Commission... Wounded* 1858. Q924.
[40] *Royal Commission... Wounded* 1858. Report page XXVII.
[41] *Medical and Surgical History...Russia* 1 Appendix IX 526-530.
[42] London Hospital House Committee minutes 1794-1801 (ref LH/A/5/16). This was a constant cry wherever water closets were introduced. Brunel's provision was generous for, at this time, five toilets were provided for four wards at the London Hospital.
[43] *Times* 19 Feb 1856.
[44] Parkes EA. *Manual of Practical Hygiene.* 439. London Churchill, 1864 quoting Medical Times & Gazette 1852. Pyaemia, commonly resulting from infected wounds, indicated extremely severe generalised infection, leading to abscesses scattered throughout the body.
[45] Wells TS TNA WO 43/991.
[46] Wells TS. *On the practical results of quarantine.* Association Medical Journal 1854;2:831-4.
[47] Army Works Corps patients may have been stationed at Renkioi or evacuated from the Crimea. They were a civilian force, not under military discipline, and not popular on account of their pay being higher than that of the soldiers. Unlike the Land Transport Corps they were muscular men. Brunton in his reminiscences mentioned the Army Works Corps being paraded for church services and taking part in his excavation at the site of Troy. When the hospital was closing he intended writing about their disposal to Sir Joseph Paxton who had organised the formation of the Works Corps (from men who had been employed in building the Great Exhibition).
[48] Parkes EA. *Report...Renkioi Hospital.* 28.
[49] TNA WO 43/991.
[50] Letter and preceding note from Florence Nightingale to Sir Harry Verney 21 November 1859.
[51] Nightingale F. *Notes on Hospitals* 3rd Ed. 10. Longman Green. London 1863. Twenty years later but well within Florence Nightingale's lifetime, 'the practice of placing patients with infectious diseases, such as smallpox, scarlet fever, measles and other communicatable diseases in the general wards of a hospital was one which could not be too strongly deprecated'. (Robins EC. *Modern Hospital Construction.* London. Parkes Museum. 1883 or the Builder 30 June 1883.)
[52] Parkes interpreted Florence Nightingale's views in the following way; the sick should be distributed over as wide an area as possible in detached, perfectly ventilated buildings, with each sick man as far from his neighbour as possible. He added that plenty of air is secured by construction and superintendence. This was true of Renkioi and, speaking of Renkioi, he added 'the effect of a great supply of air on some diseases is marvellous'. (*Manual of Practical Hygiene,* 1864.)

[53] Letter from Florence Nightingale to Sir Harry Verney 30 September 1859. At a regimental hospital, a tent partly sunk in the ground was considered to have served admirably as an operating theatre and as a place for the performance of post mortem examinations (*Medical and Surgical History...Russia* 2: 255).
[54] Rosenberg CE. (Ed.) *Florence Nightingale on Hospital Reform.* New York & London: Garland, 1989.
[55] Cope Z *Florence Nightingale and the Doctors*. 14. London: Museum Press, 1958.
[56] *Royal Commission...Sick and Wounded* 1858.

Chapter 7

The Hospital at Work

> 'It may seem a strange principle to enunciate as the very first requirement in a Hospital that it should do the sick no harm.' *Florence Nightingale*

Something must be said about the patients. The names of only five patients are known, four recorded in the *Times,* and a fifth, a sergeant, in Beddoe's autobiography. All died and nothing is known about even these as, until much later, the records of soldiers who died were destroyed. Consequently it is only possible to build up a general picture.

The first patients at Renkioi came from close by, seamen from passing ships who had fallen from the mast, or workmen who had suffered injuries or sickness, and members of the garrison and a few civilians. These were admitted during the early summer of 1855. In mid-August, Parkes wrote to John Hall to say that 500 beds were now ready for patients,[1] but the hospital did not start work in earnest until the first sick and wounded were landed from the screw steamer Imperador on October 2nd 1855.[2] Some 40 of the first batch of patients to arrive by sea had been in the attack on the Redan, a huge fortress, its capture leading to the fall of Sevastopol, the last major encounter of the war. Casualties were said to have been higher than at the storming of Badajoz in the Peninsular War. Typically a patient would have been a soldier of the line in a regiment in the Light Division such as the 19th Regiment of foot.[3] This regiment (now the Green Howards) had embarked in April 1854 with 31 officers and 913 men and reached Scutari on 12 May 1854, and then Varna on 30 May. The first two cases of cholera occurred at Varna and thereafter the regiment was dogged by cholera, diarrhoea, and dysentery. A terrible winter with a clear deterioration of the men's health was followed by some improvement in the spring. In

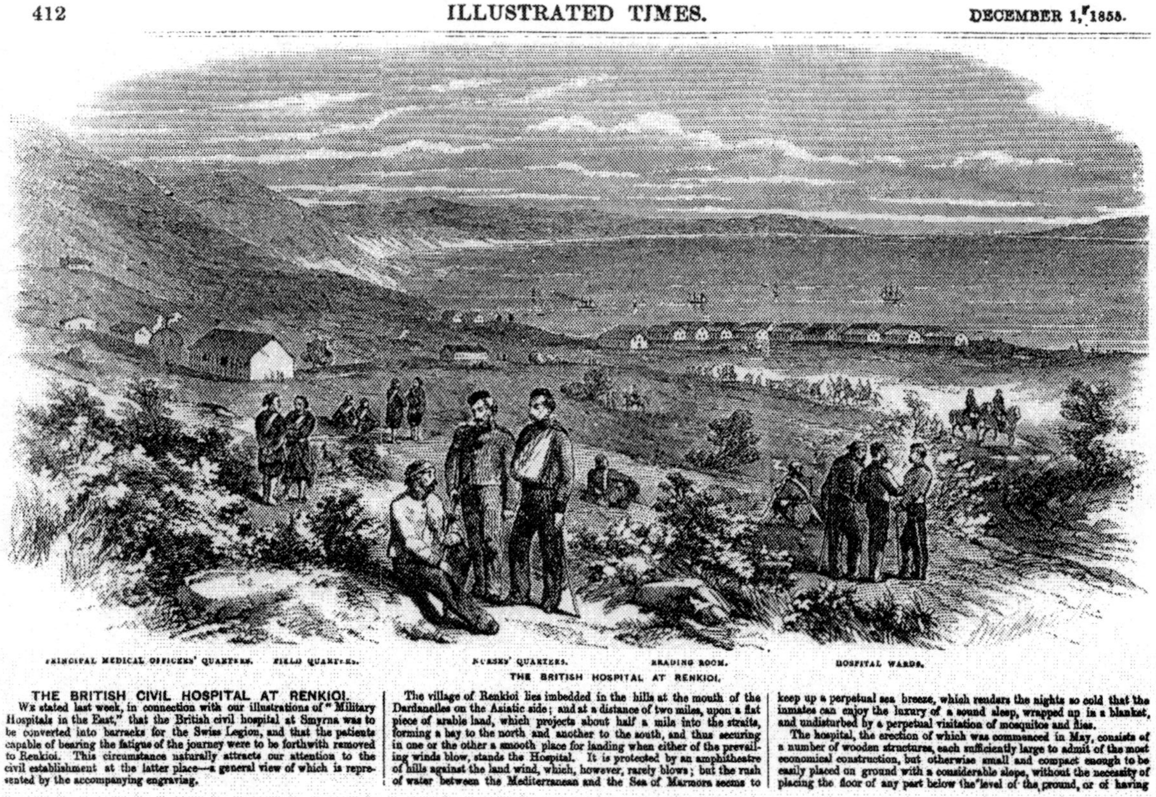

412 ILLUSTRATED TIMES. DECEMBER 1, 1855.

PRINCIPAL MEDICAL OFFICERS' QUARTERS. FIELD QUARTERS. NURSES' QUARTERS. READING ROOM. HOSPITAL WARDS.

THE BRITISH HOSPITAL AT RENKIOI.

THE BRITISH CIVIL HOSPITAL AT RENKIOI.

We stated last week, in connection with our illustrations of "Military Hospitals in the East," that the British civil hospital at Smyrna was to be converted into barracks for the Swiss Legion, and that the patients capable of bearing the fatigue of the journey were to be forthwith removed to Renkioi. This circumstance naturally attracts our attention to the civil establishment at the latter place—a general view of which is represented by the accompanying engraving.

The village of Renkioi lies imbedded in the hills at the mouth of the Dardanelles on the Asiatic side; and at a distance of two miles, upon a flat piece of arable land, which projects about half a mile into the straits, forming a bay to the north and another to the south, and thus securing in one or the other a smooth place for landing when either of the prevailing winds blow, stands the Hospital. It is protected by an amphitheatre of hills against the land wind, which, however, rarely blows; but the rush of water between the Mediterranean and the Sea of Marmora seems to keep up a perpetual sea breeze, which renders the nights so cold that the inmates can enjoy the luxury of a sound sleep, wrapped up in a blanket, and undisturbed by a perpetual visitation of mosquitos and flies.

The hospital, the erection of which was commenced in May, consists of a number of wooden structures, each sufficiently large to admit of the most economical construction, but otherwise small and compact enough to be easily placed on ground with a considerable slope, without the necessity of placing the floor of any part below the level of the ground, or of having

Figure 13: Patients at Renkioi with hospital buildings visible beyond.

Source: *Illustrated Times*, 1 December 1855.

this single regiment of some 900 men, during the whole period of active service, there were 2392 admissions to hospital, many patients being admitted on several occasions. 80 men were killed in action and 386 died from disease or wounds inflicted by the enemy. 295 men were invalided to England, and 65 discharged the service on account of disease contracted in the field, and 124 in consequence of wounds inflicted by the enemy. Among the deaths from cholera was that of the Assistant Surgeon, John Longmore, the younger brother of the Surgeon to the Regiment, Thomas Longmore, later to be Professor of Surgery at the Army Medical School. The regiment was in action at Alma, Balaklava, and Inkerman, and throughout the siege of Sevastopol, and received many reinforcements, callow youths from South Yorkshire, of the kind described in Harriet Martineau's book *England and her Soldiers*.[4]

The taking of the Redan was their last major engagement. Twenty-six men were killed, and ten officers and 129 men wounded including the commanding officer who subsequently died. Lieutenant Dunham Massy, commanding the grenadier company of the 19th Regiment of foot, acquired the nickname of 'Redan Massy' which stayed with him all his life. His bravery caught the imagination of the nation; he was 17 years of age.[5]

The attack makes a grim story. On that day there were 273 admissions to the Camp General Hospital, the hospital in the Crimea immediately behind the front line. All were from the Light Division (in which the 19th Regiment of Foot was serving) and the Second Division. Though not verifiable, some wounded of the 19th Regiment could well have been evacuated to Renkioi which by now was ready to receive patients by the shipload. Dr Charles Maunder, a Civil Surgeon (who had just come from Renkioi, having volunteered for service in the Crimea), on his first day 'in Camp', tended a Russian prisoner and staunched the bleeding from his facial wound by tying a ligature round the common carotid artery in the neck. Advice about the patient was given by Dr Mouat, who was to be the first medical officer awarded the Victoria Cross, and the case was reported in the Lancet.[6] The patient died next day and a post-mortem examination was carried out.

Harriet Martineau (1802-1876), a brilliant journalist, took up the cudgels for the ordinary soldier after the war, emphasising not only his bravery, but the need for his proper recognition by society. She painted a picture of the British soldier with his lack of education and frequent drunkenness. She described the lot of the recruit, typically a poor farm boy, on eight shillings a week, now living in a hovel on the farm, who looks forward to a better

Table 2 Hospital ships arriving at Renkioi October 1855- February 1856

Name of ship & tonnage	Sick	wounded	From	Sailed	Arrived Renkioi	Disembarkation Began	Disembarkation Completed	No of attendants Sgts	Orderlies
Imperador 1800	183	32	Balaklava	28 Sept 1855	Noon 2 Oct	2pm 2 Oct	3.30pm 2 Oct	2	23
Melbourne 1400	115	23	Smyrna	3pm 19 Nov	6pm 20 Nov	10am 21 Nov	noon 21 Nov	2	23
Melbourne	78	2	Smyrna	4am 25 Nov	11.30pm 25 Nov	1.30pm 26 Nov	2.30pm 26 Nov	2	23
Melbourne	16	1	Smyrna	4pm 1 Dec	6pm 2 Dec	7.30pm 3 Dec	7.45pm 3 Dec	2	23
Gibraltar 660	110	0	Balaklava	16 Dec	18 Dec	2pm 18 Dec	2.30pm 18 Dec	1	17
Melbourne 1400	122	0	Balaklava	9 Jan 1856	14 Jan 1856	11.30am 15 Jan	1,30pm 15 Jan	1	15
Andes 770	97	0	Balaklava	19 Jan	23 Jan	4pm 23 Jan	5.30pm 23 Jan	1	15
Alps 770	119	1	Balaklava	25 Jan	-	-	-	1	14
Gibraltar 660	100	3	Balaklava	4 Feb	7 Feb	4pm 7 Feb	5pm 7 Feb	1	10
Melbourne 1400	120	1	Balaklava	8 Feb	10 Feb	3.30pm 11 Feb	4.15pm 11 Feb	1	14
Total	1060	63							

Source: *Medical and Surgical History… Russia* 1858. 2: 480

life if he joins the army, with better clothes than he has ever worn, better food with meat every day, and never before able to keep himself so clean. But the reality is different. The clothes that look so good suck up water like a sponge and shrink, his boots burst out before he has worn them a week, boiled beef he cannot face, and the water is bad to drink. Everything about him in the barracks is horrible, and worst of all his health deteriorates. Men of his age in civil life died at the rate of seven per thousand every year, but the soldier's death rate at home was 20 per thousand.[7] The more familiar picture was of men whose character gave the army a bad name, 'wretched individuals, the profligate unreclaimable sons of gentlemen, who having spent their patrimony, offended their friends, and estranged themselves from society.'

George Macleod, the Civil Surgeon who worked at Smyrna and subsequently with distinction in the Crimea (Chapters 2 and 4) and was well known to some at Renkioi, gives a good idea of how surgeons saw their patients. He described the soldier as a patient:

> unlike the civilian in many points. In some things he may be said to be a better patient, and in many he is decidedly worse. Some of these points of distinction should always be borne in mind in estimating the comparative success of surgery as practised in the case of one or the other.
>
> In the soldier's favour, we have physically, his being generally in the prime of life, and in robust health. Morally, his receiving the wound which brings him under treatment in the discharge of his duty; his 'honourable scars' recognise none of those causes referrible to misconduct, which so frequently make the civilian the inmate of an hospital. He has, moreover, no fear, like the civilian, for the future, if incapacitated for further employment, as he knows his country will provide for him, and look on him with gratitude. So far the soldier has the advantage; but then, in general, how irregular and debauched is his life, and how apt to occasion that 'debility of excess', which conceals a constitution weak to resist injury, under an outward appearance of strength and vigour.[8]

Parkes' opinion of the British soldier was short but to the point: 'I know that no men are so manageable as English soldiers when properly treated and when spirits are kept from them.'[9]

Table 2 shows shipping movements and the numbers of military patients (NCOs and other ranks) transferred; officers transferred from Smyrna were not recorded. After the arrival of the Imperador on October 2nd 1855, the number of further landings only amounted to nine; the last took place on 10th February 1856. Thereafter, any new admissions (some 30 in all) were similar to those of the first months and there were no more after June 1856.

From the Crimea to Renkioi usually took three or four days. Seven voyages were between Balaklava and Renkioi, and three were from Smyrna when that hospital closed. None of the voyages were directly from the Crimea; there was always a stop at Scutari. At Scutari some NCOs and men were put ashore and others brought on board. All officers disembarked. While there were occasional admissions of officers from the locality, the only officers ever transferred to Renkioi appear to have come from Smyrna. The Imperador carried seven sick officers and 188 sick men from Balaklava to Scutari but left Scutari for Renkioi with 183 sick men and 32 wounded men, but no officers. Allocated to wards appropriately by the Divisional doctors overseeing disembarkation, delay in unloading was always minimal. Not every patient needed to be carried to the wards; in the first disembarkation, all walked apart from eight or ten who were carried on stretchers.[10] The Crimea was 500 miles (800 km), and Scutari 100 miles (160 km) from Renkioi but by this stage of the war, the hazards of the voyage had been greatly reduced. There were four deaths on these voyages, three before Scutari, and one between Scutari and Renkioi. The situation was quite different from that a year or more earlier when 114 patients, out of a total of 318 on board the Caduceus died on the voyage from the Crimea to Scutari.[11] Now there was a splendid line of steamers established between the Crimea and the Bosphorus.

The railway with its horse-drawn wagons for moving patients from ship to ward was a brilliant innovation, as this extract from the *Times* shows:

> *Times*, The British Hospital at Renkioi. Our own correspondent. Renkioi Jan. 31 1856
>
> On the 28th a large vessel was seen steering direct for the south pier through a heavy mist of rain; she proved to be the Alps, with 120 invalids from Balaklava, and orders were given for their immediate disembarkation. The medical officers went

> to their respective posts, strong fatigue parties of soldiers were ordered out by Major Chads, the military officer in command, and a proper number of wards were put into their usual state of comfort. At one end a large stove blazes cheerfully; at the other water, arrowroot, and other necessaries are kept hot and ready in Price's candle stoves; lights are suspended along the walls, and a requisite number of nurses and orderlies are seen busily occupied in arranging furniture and bedding. Of the rapidity with which matters at Renkioi are conducted an idea may be formed when I state that the Alps dropped anchor off the south pier at 3.30 p.m., the first boat left the ship's side, about half a mile from the shore, at 4, and every patient was in bed and under treatment, having been dieted and prescribed for by the proper medical officer, by 5.20. It is above a quarter of a mile from the south pier to the corridor. Rain fell heavily, the ground was soft and muddy, and the daylight was gone at 5, and yet the men were deposited in their beds warm and dry, and without fatigue. The accomplishment of this was due to the railway, which now runs from the pier to the corridor, where a turntable receives it, ready in a few weeks to direct the carriages upon branch lines which will bring them to the very door of the wards. Instead of patients being carried singly upon stretchers, between two men staggering over the rough wild country, with their worn-out and groaning burden, 50 or 60 men are put upon trucks, covered up with blankets, and galloped into the hospital along the smooth tramway in a few minutes. Never was a more successful work undertaken, and it will remain a matter of history that the first railway ever laid down in Asia Minor was on the plain of the Renkioi Hospital, and used as a transport for sick and wounded soldiers during the campaign in the Crimea.[12]

A total of 1408 patients were admitted to Renkioi Hospital, 1331 military and 87 others, e.g. sailors injured in accidental falls, and Turkish and Greek workmen. 1123 of the military patients were brought to Renkioi by sea, and 208 admitted from the locality. The table in Appendix 5 shows, according to diagnosis, the number of patients admitted and the number of deaths.

Medical patients accounted for rather more than three quarters of the admissions. Of the total of 50 deaths of military patients, 22 were ascribed to fever, 14 to chronic dysentery, eight to phthisis pulmonalis and one to pyaemia caused by wounds, one to frostbite, and one to each of four other causes. Thus only one death was ascribed to wounds. Parkes found the most distressing cases were those of frostbite with gangrene of the extremities, sometimes of both hands and feet. In some cases the areas affected by frostbite had separated off and in others amputation, perhaps multiple, would be necessary.

Fevers, only qualified as intermittent or continued, dysentery, and rheumatic conditions caused most sickness, and even a single one of these conditions was responsible for more admissions than injury. Most common were fevers, especially 'the well known spotted typhus with a marked eruption' but not a high mortality; it was often not possible to distinguish true typhus from typhoid and other forms of 'continued fever'. In the official figures (Table 2) neither Typhus nor Typhoid appear, only 'continued fever', emphasising the difficulty of deciding on an exact diagnosis. Typhoid as the diagnosis appeared in this report in the *Times*:

> There was only one death, already reported, during the whole of the month of November. One of the Jagers (German Legion) has since died from water on the chest. He was admitted labouring under typhoid fever of the most severe character; this febrile attack passed away, but general dropsy, dependent on internal organic disease of some standing, supervened and he expired rather suddenly. I hear on all sides that Dr Bader (a German by birth, but one of the Renkioi staff) who had the care of these men exhibited no common amount of skill, every case being very severe and presenting peculiarities of its own. The unremitting attention of the nurses also deserves notice and praise.[13]

On admission, some patients showed mild scurvy but recovered, no doubt due to that unremitting attention and, in particular, a good diet including fresh vegetables. Only milk was in short supply.

Parkes saw a difference between patients from Regiments of the Line, such as the 19th Regiment of Foot, whose experiences of the campaign and exploits at the Redan have been described and whose physical standards were good, and those from the Land Transport Corps. The Land Transport Corps had been formed a year after the start of the war to meet transport needs, and after the war was to become permanent as the Military Train. These men were often of inferior physique or too old or too young, and regarded as undisciplined. Their status was inferior so that although the orders for huts to house them in the Crimea were among the first to be made, these huts came to be amongst the last to be supplied.[14] Consequently the men of the Transport Corps spent the second winter of the war, very

Figure 14: 'Arabs' of the Land Transportation Corps.
Photograph previously attributed to Dr. Kirk, but most probably taken by Dr. Robertson. By permission of the owner.

hard at work in very exposed conditions. In the Crimea, separate and inferior hospitals were opened entirely for their use. Their degraded status now appears deplorable, but worse off still was the auxiliary force of 'natives', Turks, Italians, and Spanish and other races attached to the Land Transport Corps and recruited in Asia Minor. When they became ill they were not admitted to army hospitals, but to inferior accommodation or were invalided and discharged from the service.

Parkes noticed similarities between these men of the Transport Corps and patients from the previous winter he had seen at Scutari on his arrival in Turkey, who had been generally ill, prostrated and scorbutic, with poor physique and much lower standards of cleanliness. Three hundred and thirty-one admissions (24.9%) were of men from the LTC compared to 1000 from Regiments of the Line. Of the 50 deaths at Renkioi, 27 were of patients from the Transport Corps, a mortality of 8.12 %, compared with 23 of patients from Regiments of the Line, a mortality of 2.3 %. Compared to the Barrack hospital at Scutari, the number of LTC patients at Renkioi was disproportionately high. Various explanations can be offered. The decision about who should be evacuated was made by senior medical officers.[15] Medical officers at Scutari may have discriminated and preferred to treat soldiers of the Line, keeping them and passing on men from the Land Transport Corps of whom they thought less well. Alternatively they may have felt that patients in the Land Transport Corps needed longer convalescence, more easily provided at Renkioi. Or it may have been that Land Transport Corps units were stationed locally. Photographs taken at Renkioi show officers of the Land Transport Corps, likely to be stationed nearby, for instance at Dardanelles (now Çanakkale) where there was a large contingent. Shown with them are sometimes 'Arabs' and 'natives' who were probably not admitted to the Hospital and for which returns were never made.

Later wars were to see the emergence of patients with 'shell-shock', hysterical symptoms such as paralysis, or anxiety states without demonstrable physical basis. The less sophisticated patients of the Crimean War experienced fear or were detected as malingering. Malingering, though stated to be quite common elsewhere, was considered rare at Renkioi; just two or three patients came to Parkes' mind.[16] There is a hint in Dr Goodeve's Divisional Report, of these matters, for he noted that rheumatic pains were common, in one patient associated with hypochondricises (sic), and in some simulated.[17] The pains were very intractable using a variety of treatments, which included the uncomfortable treatment of cupping.

A case report by Carl Bader,[18] named above in the *Times* extract, indicates the standard of care at Renkioi. It is such a clear account of the situation and the attitudes and expectations of those at Renkioi that it is quoted almost in full.

'Case of Tracheotomy. Performed successfully after the pulse and respiration had ceased.' The surgery and its successful outcome must have seemed as satisfactory to Bader as it would to any young surgeon of the present day.

On the 28th of April last, at 1.30p.m., being Orderly Officer of the day, I was hastily called to see a man 29 years of age, who was said to be in a fit. I found him lying on the floor in a state of unconsciousness. His comrades told me that he had made a bet to eat a large quantity of meat in a very short time, and in the midst of his exertion he fell down and made signs to those around him to thump him on the back, which they did. When I saw him he had been unconscious for about four minutes. I found his skin cyanotic, the superficial veins swollen, and all the muscles spasmodically contracted. No respiratory movement was perceptible. The pulse could scarcely be felt, and the pupils were contracted.

Sending immediately for tracheotomy instruments, in the meantime I opened the mouth, but with great difficulty, by thrusting a ruler between the teeth. Examining the mouth and fauces, I passed my finger as far as the upper edges of the vocal chords (sic), but found nothing to obstruct the passage of air. About two or three minutes were thus lost. Although the mouth was kept open no respiratory movement ensued. The pulse disappeared altogether, while the cyanotic appearance and the muscular spasm increased. The instruments now arrived, and I proceeded to operate, more to satisfy my surgical conscience and to comply with the urgent wish of my colleague Mr Dix, who was present, than with any hope of saving the patient, as I believed him to be quite dead. We put him on a table, and I made an incision about an inch long, beginning at the cricoid cartilage. I arrived at once at the trachea, and thrust in a trochar at the lower edge of the cartilage, withdrawing it immediately and pushing on the canula [sic] until about one inch of it was in the trachea. Several seconds passed. The patient then made one inspiration, and with the expiration a quantity of frothy bloodstained mucus escaped from the canula. The inspirations then became deeper, and followed each other at shorter intervals. I assisted expiration by pressure on the abdomen. At every fourth or fifth expiration a quantity of mucus was thrown up, and after some fifteen expirations the pulse reappeared. In about half an hour the respiration and pulse became regular, and we removed the patient to the ward. He had an involuntary motion and also vomited, among a quantity of mucus, a piece of meat the size of a man's fist. After this vomiting, the breathing and circulation underwent no change. He was put to bed, quite naked, and with the head raised.

At 3 p.m. Mr Spencer Wells the Chief Surgeon saw the patient in consultation, and as he was completely comatose and the surface of the body was still cyanotic, it was determined to take 10 ounces of blood from the arm. The pulse, which had been small and very feeble, immediately became fuller and rose to 60. The head and chest were repeatedly sponged with cold water, and an attendant constantly cleared away the frothy mucus escaping from the canula during the whole night. The man remained unconscious, the respiratory movements of the thorax inconsiderable, the pulse 60 and full, and the muscular spasms continued.

April 29th – Mr Spencer Wells again saw him with me, fifteen hours after operation. The spasms and cyanosis continued. I had before this been obliged several times to free the passage from air by pressing a small piece of sponge through the canula into the trachea. This was always followed by the ejection of a large quantity of mucus and greater freedom of respiration. The current of air through the tube was strong; pulse 60, regular and full. The mouth was spasmodically closed, but on stopping the canula with the finger the air was felt to escape between the teeth. We therefore determined to remove the canula, and I did so. After withdrawing it, the air escaped by the wound, which formed a hole two lines (sic) in diameter.

It was left uncovered and an attendant continually wiped off the mucus which collected. During the day, some wine and an egg were forced into the patient's mouth and he swallowed them, but without violent coughing. The unconsciousness and muscular rigidity continued. The noise from the escaping air, and the state of the patient rendered auscultation impossible. Percussion normal. Discharge from bladder and intestines involuntary.

> 30th - Unconsciousness, and spasmodic muscular contractions continue. Egg and wine given as before. Eyes still shut, and pupils contracted.
>
> May 1st – The patient was very restless during the night, rolling from one side to the other. This morning he had an epileptic fit, which lasted half an hour. After it the rigidity of the muscles returned. The breathing was short and laborious, partly through the mouth. Pulse 90. I could not discover whether the fit had been caused by any voluntary obstruction to the passage of air. During the fit the patient, who had remained constantly stiff before, made violent movements with trunk and extremities. Towards evening he became more conscious, opening his eyes, and swallowing freely what was given him.

The patient continued to improve. He had one further epileptic fit and gradually diminishing trembling and involuntary movements. By the 14th he was walking about and his vision, initially dim had returned to normal. He was intellectually restored. The opening in the trachea closed and he was finally, 'in quite as good health as before operation'. Bader summarised his report, dated June 24th, as follows:

> The peculiar features of this case are in the first place, the recovery after apparent death, the pulse and respiratory efforts having quite ceased; and, secondly, the recovery of the intellectual faculties. The patient was completely unconscious for three days after the operation. He had two severe epileptic fits, and after this was in a condition resembling severe delirium tremens. Even after complete recovery a remarkable slowness of movement remained. In a surgical point of view, it may be remarked that, although the canula was removed fifteen hours after the operation, and the wound continued to suppurate freely, yet the pus which must have entered the trachea produced no kind of irritation on the respiratory organs.

Only one comment can be made: what a lucky man! The account could have been written yesterday, and is so detailed and accurate and by such a good observer that anyone reading it in the twenty first century can follow the details easily. The soldier, his foolishness compounded by his enormous meat ration, was lucky to be close to the surgeon rather than a quarter of a mile away along the corridor, as he easily could have been. He was more lucky still to have rapid and skilled removal of the enormous obstruction blocking his windpipe. Oddly enough, a similar operation, 22 years earlier, had been carried out on Brunel himself after he accidentally inhaled a coin during a conjuring trick. Brunel's operation, a tracheotomy performed by the distinguished surgeon, Sir Benjamin Brodie, was unsuccessful but fortunately an apparatus to invert Brunel was devised which allowed him to cough the coin out.[19] In Bader's patient, serious brain damage due to interruption of the circulation, of which his unconsciousness, rigidity and fits were a warning, at least appeared to have been prevented and the nursing was assiduous. All in all a very lucky man and how much previous experience of the operation had Bader had? Probably very little; Spencer Wells was available to give advice, cautious perhaps because there had been complaints at Smyrna of senior doctors, under-employed, unnecessarily taking cases out of the hands of their more junior colleagues.[20]

Local residents occasionally travelled 100 miles (160 km.) for advice. Parkes says, 'we were obliged in some cases, on the grounds of common humanity, to receive them into hospital' and, rather cryptically, 'the regular Government allowance for extra patients always being paid in'. However medical work among the local inhabitants was sought after; whether there was any recompense beyond the gift of delicious grapes when a patient on the sick list was visited, is not recorded. A remarkable account of pilgrims, hoping for a cure, coming from Gallipoli, Tenedos and elsewhere to the church of St George at Erenkioi, on the Saint's day, survives. The church contained a miracle-working picture of Saint George. The Renkioi doctors visited the church, to Protestant eyes arranged very incongruously, and enticed all those patients to leave whom immediate surgery would benefit, and,

> there and then gratuitously begin their cure. We have seen no less than three of these knights-coupant wandering about in search of adventure, and one especial doctor from Norwich used to reconnoitre quite regularly the ladies' bowers and when he discovered a squint or cataract he would chloroform the owner almost before he had received a fair affirmative to

> his question, thelete copse [approximating to, 'do you want a cut?', in modern Greek]. The first eye we ever saw disengaged from its socket was a Greek grey one, which Hakims [doctors] Bader, Faucus, and Dix made a present of to our raven Jack for his amusement. On one St George's afternoon five of these eye patients and their amorous sisters remained a month after the festival was over, and as they had outstaid the hospitalities of the village, we had almost to board these warm hearted pilgrims.[21]

Eye diseases were common, and their treatment much appreciated. Eleven years after Renkioi, Virchow, the great German pathologist, briefly turning from his other interests to looking after Schliemann's workforce at Troy, found eye disease common there.[22]

Parkes speaks of many operations being performed. He was very accurate and there is no reason to think that he exaggerated. At Renkioi there were no patients with very recent wounds and little urgent surgery apart from that needed after accidents occurring locally. Most of the soldiers being treated had had their injuries a few weeks before or were convalescent after a long period in hospital elsewhere. Some might need further surgery; infection was so frequent and a foreign body in the wound could make itself all too apparent sometime after injury. Wells, writing later, remarked that at Renkioi to stop bleeding, he made use of a 'bulldog' rather than fingers, to squeeze spurting or oozing blood vessels during operation. Appreciating the advantage of using an instrument rather than fingers, from the 'bulldog' he developed the artery forceps he subsequently perfected, still in use and known to this day by his name.[23] Unlike the surgeon at the front who spent his time staunching immediate bleeding, exploring wounds, removing foreign material, and draining infected wounds or dealing with secondary haemorrhage, the surgeon at Renkioi had a less onerous task. There was surgery to be done at Renkioi but it was less urgent, with all the benefits of beautiful surroundings, fresh air and sunshine, and a good diet added to good nursing care, to aid recovery.

There is no mention in Parkes' Report of anaesthesia, though it was accepted practice by this stage of the war. Sir James Y. Simpson, who had introduced the use of chloroform as an anaesthetic, taught and later recruited many of the Renkioi staff. Spencer Wells had demonstrated a new French anaesthetic apparatus to the local medical society when in Malta before the war. Anaesthesia, saving the patient from agony (and other patients from hearing the patient's screams), allowed the surgeon much more time to conduct an operation. It was usually given by the most junior doctor present and was rarely mentioned in published surgical reports. In the eye practice just described, it is clear that the use of chloroform for eye operations had begun; unfortunately with chloroform the likelihood of severe post-operative vomiting threatened the operation's success. Before the war, excision of the eyeball was undertaken without anaesthesia but the skills of the doctors at Renkioi avoided this.

Renkioi was a model hospital with a skilled staff. The tracheotomy previously described indicates the highest standards with diagnosis based on observation and an accurate history and examination. That examination was being extended. Scientific advances in chemistry, physics, anatomy, and physiology (i.e. structure and function), and pathology (i.e. disease and abnormalities) together with the microscope, were rapidly increasing the understanding of disease. At Renkioi, examination of the body after death was invariable or almost so. A microscope is not mentioned in Parkes' Report, nor apparatus for chemistry although Parkes indicated that the estimation of ozone was so unsatisfactory that it had to be abandoned. At the Barrack Hospital, Scutari, a well-equipped dissection room with microscopes became available after the visit of the Pathology Commission.

Stethoscopes with one ear piece, but not, as now, two, were included in the hospital equipment, and in his application for his post at University College Hospital, Parkes said that he was proficient in their use.[24] Parkes, when delivering the Goulstonian Lectures on fever at the Royal College of Physicians referred to instrumental temperature readings to illustrate his lecture, so that he may have included his own instrument in his luggage.[25] More than one doctor at Renkioi had had special experience of eye diseases[26] but unless doctors had brought their own, an ophthalmoscope at Renkioi seems unlikely.

Divisional reports described treatment in some detail. With few exceptions, treating the causes of disease was impracticable, and medical treatment was symptomatic. It was recognised that many treatments were ineffective[27] and that rest, warmth, and food were most important. Good nursing was so often the key to recovery. However, reports of dreadful treatments in civil practice at the time abound. At Renkioi, treatment for diarrhoeal diseases consisted of opium, astringent mixtures and, in some cases, enemas of silver nitrate or copper sulphate. A hot dry south east land wind seemed to exercise an unfavourable influence on some of the patients suffering from diarrhoea and dysentery, but gone were the limited bleedings and leeches applied to the abdomen which Parkes had advocated in 1846. Cupping for rheumatic pains is mentioned. Malaria was treated with quinine; the few cases admitted were thought not to have arisen locally.

Convalescence was very important. A simple flesh wound usually healed in one to two months, but infected wounds took much longer to heal or perhaps never did so. Single storey buildings gave easy access to the outside world and 'as soon as a man could crawl he always got into the corridor or between the houses, and the good effects were manifest. Some of the medical officers had their patients' beds carried into the corridor when the men could not walk. In the winter, greatcoats were provided for the men to put on and they were encouraged to go into the corridor'. Convalescent patients played skittles, quoits, bat and ball, draughts, backgammon, chess. Most of these were provided by the government which also paid for books and newspapers, and these arrangements were similar to those organised by Florence Nightingale at Scutari and a far cry from the situation at a civilian hospital in 1855 where the Junior Chaplain was thanked by the Weekly Board for finding a newspaper in a ward and ordering its removal.[28] After treatment in idyllic surroundings, patients were discharged back to their units, often after more convalescence at the small Civil Hospital at Abydos or while waiting at Scutari. It might take several weeks before they were back at their units.

Three hundred and twenty patients were invalided home from Renkioi. On 28th Jan 1856, the Saldanha Transport called and carried home 62 other ranks and two officers. One of these was Dr Bransby Roberts with rheumatic fever and on the staff of Renkioi Hospital, and the other, an officer of the Bashi-Bazouks with a most severe attack of dysentery.[29]

That long road home is well illustrated by a typical account of a soldier's recovery after wounding. The patient eventually came under the care of James Syme, Professor of Clinical Surgery at Edinburgh. In this particular case the journey was from Scutari, not Renkioi, but a connection with Renkioi exists for Syme was the admired teacher of some of the Scottish graduates at Renkioi. Syme was a brilliant surgeon, the father-in-law of Joseph Lister, and exceptionally quarrelsome. He was said, 'never to have wasted a word or a drop of ink or a drop of blood', and to have been able to perform an amputation through the hip joint in 90 seconds. Syme and Parkes were also briefly colleagues at University College before the war and, some years after the war, worked together considering how subjects required by the newly formed General Medical Council should be taught to medical students with most advantage. They disagreed on many points. In the course of an equable debate, Parkes remarked that 'Mr Syme was, perhaps, the very best teacher of surgery in the world'. Syme, direct, as usual, and often differing from Parkes, observed that: 'Dr Parkes would treat medical students as infants, and supply them with wet nurses'.[30]

The patient's history was as follows: Sergeant J.H. 23d Royal Welsh Fusiliers, aged 28, was wounded at the battle of Alma, on 20th September 1854.[31] He was struck by a ball from the enemy's column, not more than ten yards in front. Feeling acute pain in the left knee, he supposed it was 'smashed', but found everything all right there.

> He, therefore, loosened his trousers, and discovered that there was a wound in the groin, whence the blood freely escaped, partly in a double jet and partly in a continuous stream. To stop the flow, he wrapped a stone in his handkerchief and secured it over the orifice by the strap of his water bottle. He was then able to rise from the ground, on which he had fallen, and fire repeatedly at the Russians, but feeling the limb extremely painful, could stand no longer, and therefore rolled himself down the slope to the bank of the river, where he again made an attempt to walk, in order to ford the stream, which proved so deep and strong, that he would have drowned unless some soldiers on the other side had given their assistance. They pulled him out and laid him on some straw, where he remained without any medical aid, until three o'clock next morning, when a surgeon dressed his wound. In the course of the same day, when almost unconscious from weakness, he was put on board a ship for Scutari, where he arrived on the 27th, and on the 1st of October, had the dressings changed for the first time since they were applied on the banks of the Alma. Some bleeding a few days afterwards, but was suppressed by pressure.

On 10th October, a piece of cartridge paper was discharged from the wound, and about the same time, an abscess was opened from which much matter and pieces of his coat and shirt escaped. On Christmas day he sailed for England and arrived on 21st January at Fort Pitt (the army hospital at Chatham). There, attempts at finding a foreign body failed and the wound remained infected, leading to secondary haemorrhage and, later, weakening of an artery wall which stretched to form an aneurysm. All this was very dangerous but a ligature applied to a nearby artery led to clotting of the aneurysm. The patient improved and was discharged on crutches on 24th May.

Soon after, he was admitted to the Edinburgh Royal Infirmary, coming under the care of Professor Syme. He appeared in good general health, but still suffered from the wound in his hip. Syme readily extracted a bullet. The wound then speedily healed. Syme concluded by saying that the operation at Fort Pitt reflected great credit on the gentlemen there and then rather wryly added: 'It may, however, be remarked that if the ball had been removed at an earlier period, there might have been no occasion for any such energetic interference, since the wound would then have probably healed, and prevented the alarming haemorrhage.' Treatment had lasted rather more than a year.

The loss to the army of a soldier on health grounds was the loss of a trained man and as great a loss as by death. The ending of the story was often the granting of a pension. That of Lieutenant Massy of the 19th foot, the regiment referred to earlier, was an example.[32]

Comparison of Renkioi with Scutari is revealing. Renkioi resembled a modern hospital much more than it did the military hospitals of the Peninsular War. Scutari had no such claim. The Scutari hospitals consisted of the giant Barrack Hospital, the General Hospital, the Hyder Pasha Palace for Officers, and hulks in the Bosphorus used for convalescent patients. Two miles to the north was the large hospital at Kuleli. All were open at somewhat different times for varying periods. The Barrack hospital, open from June 1854 until June 1856, was much the largest, and was most closely associated with Florence Nightingale. Barrack Hospital and Scutari were almost synonymous terms.

Scutari and Renkioi have been compared, quoting a mortality of 42% at Scutari compared to 3% at Renkioi.[33] This rightly emphasises the contrast between the two, Scutari dreadful at its worst period, Renkioi in its short life, late in the war, the reverse. However this comparison is misleading and a much better one is when both hospitals were open at the same time, in the second year of the war; then the situation at Scutari was utterly different from earlier.

In the first year of the war, the number of patients who had passed through Scutari was enormous. At one point nearly 5000 beds were occupied and the hospitals were overwhelmed. Patients were so numerous that there was no time to register their particulars on arrival. They were brought by ship from the Crimea, often after delays and in dreadful conditions and, on disembarkation, faced further delays, overcrowded wards, an appalling sanitary state, and an exhausted staff, hampered by administrative incompetence.

It was into this that Florence Nightingale stepped on November 4th 1854 when she arrived at Scutari. Improvement began and then came the very important work of the Sanitary Commission, commencing in March 1855.[34] With less fighting in the Crimea, the number of wounded fell and, with the close of the first cholera epidemic (Figure 5), the number of sick also fell, and overcrowding ceased to be a problem.

Conditions should only be compared after September 1855 when both Scutari and Renkioi were open simultaneously (Table 3). Before Renkioi opened, 37159 were admitted to Scutari and Kuleli with 5149 deaths (13.9%). Admissions were much fewer between October 1855 and June 1856, only 6009 admissions with 283 deaths (4.7%), compared to 1331 admissions with 50 deaths (3.76 %) at Renkioi.[35] Wounds accounted for 333 admissions and four deaths at Scutari, and 93 admissions with one death at Renkioi.

Table 3: Admissions and Deaths at the Hospitals

	Renkioi		Scutari and Kuleli	
	Admissions	Deaths	Admissions	Deaths
Jun 54-Sep 55	–	–	37159	5149
Oct 1855	232	6	1187	44
Nov	234	1	1124	163
Dec	263	5	724	29
Jan 1856	345	12	448	20
Feb	226	16	279	7
Mar	11	9	595	8
Apr	4	1	737	8
May	8	0	586	1
Jun	7	0	329	3
Oct 55-Jun 56	1330	50	6009	283
Jun 54-Jun 56	–	–	43168	5432

Source: *Medical Surgical History… Russia*. Returns 1. *General Hospitals in the Bosphorus* and Nightingale F. *Notes on Hospitals*. 1859 Note F.

At the outset Renkioi was quite busy, with the most activity in January and February 1856. Soon additional beds (including those at Renkioi), became available but remained largely unused. Admissions to Scutari fell and now there was little need for relief; from March 1856, the Renkioi staff found themselves at leisure.

A Civil Surgeon, Peter Pinkoffs, was working at Scutari during the last twelve months of the war and left a picture of conditions in the Barrack Hospital during the time that Renkioi Hospital was open.[36] He gave full credit to Miss Nightingale and considered cleanliness and food very satisfactory. A majority of patients had been under treatment for three or four weeks 'up at the front'. Judging from his own cases, about 70 per cent of patients being treated at Scutari were convalescent from fever, diarrhoea, dysentery, and rheumatism. A generous but not too stimulating diet and proper hygienic measures were the treatment most required. There were few wounded as the majority were sent direct to England. The remaining 30 per cent of patients consisted of patients from the depot or troops fresh from England and, with the exception of the cholera victims, only a few were acutely ill.

There was one obvious difference between the two hospitals during this period: cholera at Scutari but not at Renkioi. In 1855, after a summer and autumn almost free from cholera, an outbreak occurred at Scutari, first in nearby villages, and then amongst the German Legion and the Osmanli Horse Artillery, who, for the most part, were living in insanitary accommodation in the eastern wing of the hospital buildings. Suddenly 150 victims of cholera were admitted between November 14th and 17th. In all, 218 patients developed cholera of whom 138 died, a mortality of 63%. At first all were admissions from outside the hospital but soon patients already in the wards, together with 16 orderlies and Dr Wood, Acting Assistant Surgeon, and Mr Beveridge, dispenser of medicines, also developed cholera. Dr Wood and Mr Beveridge succumbed to the disease within a few hours.[37] Dr MacGrigor and Dr John Mayne also died. There was a rumour that Dr Summers had died but he survived until 1897. The course of the illness was very short and nearly half the deaths occurred within twelve hours of the onset of the illness. Expert advice was obtained from the Sanitary Commission, working there.

At Renkioi, in contrast, there was no cholera. Cholera, primarily a waterborne infection, is also spread by food contaminated by human excreta. At Scutari the hospital water supply was considered satisfactory but drainage and sanitation were still unsatisfactory. Discipline was less good than at Renkioi; in the summer of 1856, Hall, on his way to England, noted that although patent water closets had by then been fitted in the Barrack Hospital; all but two were out of order.[38] Had cholera been brought to Renkioi, with its effective sanitary precautions, how many patients already in the wards would have become infected and would the staff have been infected? A critical question that can have no answer.

Whether the patients at Scutari and Renkioi were comparable is impossible to know. With treatment mainly symptomatic, and medicinal treatment so ineffective, a good diet and good nursing, by now available at both, gave the patient the best chance. Mortality at Scutari, including that due to cholera, was 4.7 %. If cholera is put aside, the percentage of deaths from all causes at Scutari falls to 2.5%, even lower than the low rate at Renkioi (3.76%) and proof of the improvement at Scutari.

[1] Letter dated 13 Aug 1855. Papers of Sir John Hall. RAMC 397 FRR2/6a. Wellcome Contemporary Medical Archives Centre.

[2] *Times* 20 October 1855. There were no officers among those landed and officers were scarcely ever treated at Renkioi. A few officers were transferred from Smyrna when that hospital closed. Occasionally an officer from a local unit was treated at Renkioi. At the end of the Napoleonic wars sick and wounded officers were usually treated in private houses but at Scutari there were officers' wards. It is likely that officers preferred to remain at Scutari, close to the excitements of Constantinople

[3] *Medical and Surgical History...Russia*.1.192-7.

[4] Martineau H. *England and her soldiers*. London: Smith Elder, 1859.

[5] Powell G. *The Green Howards* 63. London: Hamish Hamilton, 1968.

[6] Guthrie GJ. *The Crimean army. Wounds of the head*. Lancet. 1856, 1: 311.

[7] Martineau H. *England and her soldiers*. 37-39. London: Smith Elder, 1859.

[8] Macleod G. *Notes on the Surgery of the War*. Edinburgh Med J 1856;1. 985

[9] Parkes EA. *Report... Renkioi Hospital* 33, 1858.

[10] *Times* 20 Oct 1855.

[11] *Medical and Surgical History...Russia* 2. 465. 1858.

[12] *Times* 19 February 1855. No stoves are visible in the plans of Renkioi Hospital and a 'log stove blazing' was not in accord with Brunel's views about fire hazards.
[13] *Times* Dec 25 1855. The names of patients who died at Renkioi are unknown apart from those given in a *Times* report (19 Feb 1855). These were as follows: Private Richard Flavel (gelatio, diarrhoea), Private Stephen Balls (fever), Private Ephraim Brown (pneumonia), and Private Joseph Winterbottom (dysentry). None appear to have been wounded. If death terminated service, the soldiers' records were destroyed.
[14] *Medical and Surgical History...Russia*. 1. 462.
[15] *Parliamentary Papers* Vol. xiii, Select Committee on the Medical Department of the Army. Q3490.
[16] *Royal Commission...Sick and Wounded 1858*. London. Stationery Office. 1858. Question 948.
[17] TNA WO 43/991.
[18] Bader C. *Case of Tracheotomy*. Lancet 1856; 2: 85-86.
[19] *Times* 16 May 1843.
[20] Shepherd J. *The Crimean Doctors* 2: 433. Liverpool: Liverpool University Press, 1991.
[21] Rattlebrain (William Eassie). *Romaic Beauties and Trojan Humbugs*. 92. London: William Tweedie, 1858.
[22] Rather LJ. *A Commentary of the Medical Writings of Rudolf Virchow*. 167. San Francisco: Norman Publishing, 1990.
[23] Spencer Wells *British Medical Journal* 1879. 1.927. Bulldog clips obstructed the blood flow temporarily and allowed the vessel to be tied when necessary. Also D'Arcy Power Selected Writings 1877-1930. 249-55. Oxford: Clarendon Press, 1931.
[24] Application for the post of Professor of Clinical Medicine and of Physician at University College. 26 June 1849. University College London Library.
[25] Parkes EA. *Gulstonian Lectures, On Pyrexia. Medical Times and Gazette* 1855: 233, 279, 331,472, 535, 561. Clinical thermometers were in use at University College Hospital in 1852 for some of Parkes' patients.
[26] Spencer Wells' first experience of surgery had been of eye conditions. Bransby Roberts worked at the London Ophthalmic Hospital before Renkioi. Bader in 1857 became. Curator of the Pathological Museum at Moorfields Eye Hospital.
[27] Conjectures about treatment abounded; these could be followed or resisted. There was always the wish to do more and the medical journals of the time are littered with accounts of useless remedies, some doing harm.
[28] Gibson AG. *The Radcliffe Infirmary*. 197. Oxford: Oxford University Press, 1926.
[29] *Times* 19 February 1856.
[30] *General Council of Medical Education and Registration*. 1868 Lancet. 1. 814-818.

[31] Syme J. *Cases and Observations in Surgery. No 1 Gunshot wounds and haemorrhage*. 1856. *Edinburgh Medical Journal* 1856 2.1. Syme also cited another case of which he was aware, of a gentleman wounded in a duel some ten years before.
[32] TNA WO 43/1057. Massy's injuries to his leg were equivalent to its loss .The decision was made, and confirmed by Lord Panmure, that the pension should be for £100 per annum, as although a Lieutenant, certificates were received from the Crimea that he was in temporary command of the Company and drawing allowance and forage as Captain.
[33] Thompson JD, Goldin G. *The Hospital: A Social and Architectural History* 155. New Haven and London: Yale University Press, 1975.
[34] *Report to the Rt Hon Lord Panmure. The Proceedings of the Sanitary Commission 1855-6*. London: Harrison and Son, 1857.
[35] 1331 was the figure in Parkes' own Report.
[36] Pinkoffs P. *Experiences of a Civilian in Eastern Military Hospitals*. 35. London: Williams and Norgate, 1857. Pinkoffs, a Civil Surgeon employed at Scutari, gave an excellent appraisal of the Civil Surgeons.
[37] Shepherd J. *Crimean War Doctors* 2.528. Liverpool: Liverpool University Press, 1991.
[38] Hall J. *Observations on difficulties in the Crimean War experienced by the Medical Department.* Wellcome Contemporary Medical Archives Centre. Papers of Sir John Hall. RAMC 397 FRT-2.

Chapter 8

Life at Renkioi

'The neighbourhood was a cross between an old historical country and a raw colony.'

Dr. John Beddoe

Life at Renkioi was safe and not unpleasant. A little defensively, as there were rumours that the civil hospitals were having an easy time, the *Times* correspondent emphasised that conditions were simple and not luxurious, with only the essentials provided.[1] Building proceeded continuously on the large hospital site, 'the sound of the hammer in all directions'.[2]

Besides huts, the water supply, drains, landing stages, and railway had to be constructed, and this work continued throughout the life of the hospital. At the start, conditions cannot have been comfortable. For a short time the medical staff were accommodated in the village of Erenkioi. The first wooden hut to be completed, was allotted to Beddoe and to Christison, perhaps because they were suffering, respectively, from diarrhoea and 'ague', so that the excitement of being in Asia Minor and the beauty of the surroundings may not have filled their thoughts to the exclusion of all else. The weather was soon hot despite sea breezes, temperatures varying in the course of the year from 25° to 90° F., and throughout their stay there was more rain than was usual. There were some reminders of the war besides the patients in the wards. 'A dog, found in the streets of Sebastopol and appearing thoroughly cowed, having probably not yet got the sound of explosions of shells and mines out of his ears, has been brought to the hospital; also a Russian prescription picked up in the Crimea by Dr Cowan of Renkioi Hospital, the principal ingredient of which was anti-scorbutic beer, scurvy being rife among the Russian soldiers, as it was among the allied troops'.[3]

During its brief existence, from May 1855 to July 1856, the hospital was sited in an exceptionally beautiful area on the shores of the Dardanelles. The *Times* compared the scene to a vast amphitheatre, the slopes dotted with woods, scrub and cultivated terraces. In the woods were Turkish oaks, pines, firs, juniper, arbutus, and other shrubs, and on the terraces wheat, barley, Indian corn, grapes, and vegetables. There was thyme underfoot, and shells and fossils at the base of a huge limestone landslip, gleaming through the trees and high on the hills. The Dardanelles, always busy, was thronged with ships of all kinds and sizes, screw and paddle steamers, and sailing ships.

The first ship bearing wounded arrived on October 1st 1855, before the first of the two landing stages had been completed. Brunton however, always equal to any situation, ran out into the sea and with the help of his navvies, in the space of a quarter of an hour, had a firm platform in operation, capable of supporting any number of people.[4] At an early stage, Parkes asked for additional buildings, including a church and Roman Catholic chapel, but the idea was immediately rejected by the War Office in London.[5] He was told that no deviation from Brunel's plan was permissible, and that conversion of a hut should meet the need. This was the only occasion on which Parkes' judgement was called in question. About the same time, Lord Stratford de Redcliffe, the British Ambassador in Constantinople, had to be persuaded not to pursue the idea of using the *Times* Fund, collected for the soldiers' comfort by the British public, to build, with the permission of the Sultan, a giant garrison church in Constantinople.[6] With the same aim of improving the soldier's lot, but a different approach, Florence Nightingale, used part of the Fund to open the Inkerman Club at Scutari. This was a social club set up to prevent widely prevailing drunkenness, by offering wholesome food, with spirits only served mixed with water. At Renkioi on Sundays, there was a service in one of the huts; at one such service, Parkes read the lessons and Brunton gave a sermon from the *Edinburgh Christian Magazine*.[7] Brunton had his men of the Army Works Corps marched to church every Sunday, and the services were soon attended by all the Europeans.[8] The hospital chaplains were the Reverend D'Arcy Preston, and the Roman Catholic priest, the Reverend J Mahe. Both appear in photographs taken by Dr Robertson.

The medical staff had their own mess which they shared with the administrative staff, the two engineers, and the officer of the garrison. The officers' mess, the roof of which was, exceptionally, tiled with local tiles, was a 'very handsome messroom', and at meals Parkes sat at the head of the table. The mess had journals such as Blackwood's and medical periodicals and quarterly journals. Books received were circulated and later sold by auction. At the end of the war, those remaining were sent back to England for use in garrison libraries. Meals were important; breakfast at 7.30, the midday meal at 2 o'clock, and tea or a mixed tea and supper with meat and eggs at 8 o'clock. Bransby Roberts, Assistant Surgeon, writing to his wife-to-be, speaks of dressing for the midday meal[9] though there was less stuffiness and ceremonial than in England.[10] Servants paid by the officers and shared, served at meal times and had been brought from England. The officers supplemented their rations with fowls, fish, ham, and bacon for which they paid. Vegetables were abundant, and only milk was in short supply because the contract that had been arranged was ineffectual, though milk would have been readily available at the Calvert's farm.[11] The contract system was a matter of great interest to the *Times* correspondent who had resided in Turkey long enough to know how business was done; he made some elaborate calculations to show the profits made by Turkish contractors. The horses of the Bashi-Bazouks stationed at Dardanelles were originally supplied with forage at 1s 10d per diem though this had been reduced to 1s 6d. The correspondent calculated that the cost of barley and chopped straw allowed a profit of 6d per day, so that, in a year, a contractor supplying the 5000 horses of the Bashi-Bazouks, those of the camp followers, and the pack horses, would make a profit of £40,000 to £50,000. Shoeing a horse cost 6d per hoof. A contractor took on this duty at a charge of 1s a hoof. As there were 5000 horses, each requiring quite frequent attention, the income to the contractor, the *Times* correspondent calculated, would have equalled, from this source alone, the pay of a bankruptcy commissioner or some similar legal dignitary in England. At Renkioi, the medical officers paid 1s 6d for a fowl which would cost 1s bought directly from a peasant. Eggs cost 1¾d or 2d each but were fresher and better in the village of Renkioi at ¾d to 1d. The advantage of the contract system should have been a steady supply, but this was not so 'I believe that were Dr Parkes not fettered by these contracts this would be the cheapest managed hospital as well as, certainly, one of the best.'[12]

The nurses ate separately. Amongst them was Miss Parkes, a volunteer and unpaid, classified as a Lady Sister. Bransby Roberts, in his letters to his fiancée, Milly, in October 1855, said that he and Dr Stretton were introduced to Miss Parkes (her post erroneously described by Dr Roberts as Lady Superintendent), and that the lady nurses, not appearing to trust the doctors, dined elsewhere. They were located in another ward as their quarters were not yet ready. Ungallantly, but perhaps to set his fiancée's mind at rest, he then goes on to say that the nurses' fears were unnecessary as 'there is only one who is not very plain, Miss Parkes', who seemed a ladylike, quick kind of girl, not very young. The others appeared neither young nor pretty. The Hospital plan shows 'Ladies Quarters' and 'Nurses', one large and one small hut, separately labelled and probably described by the *Times* as 'two detached buildings'.[13] Another building, close to the Hospital reservoir, is labelled 'artizans', for the 18 skilled workmen who came out from England with Brunton. The hospital laundry, shown on the plan, not only dealt with the patients' clothing and hospital linen, but also that of the staff, the officers, officers' wives, nurses, artizans etc. who paid for this service. No buildings were shown on the plan for the Greek and Turkish workmen; they lived in their own homes outside the hospital.

Dr Parkes had his own house, built on a slight hill, where he lived with his wife. There were other wives about too; Wells, Goodeve, Holmes Coote, and Hale also had their wives with them. Mrs Wells and Mrs Holmes Coote each gave birth to a daughter in November.[14] Mr Brunton's hut was near the south pier; he shared it with Dr Robertson so they were both well placed when a hospital ship unloaded. Brunton was joined in the late summer by his wife and son, whom the War Office authorised to be his assistant.

Dr Parkes invited the civil and military Pashas of the Dardanelles to inspect the hospital on Sept 24 1855. The party was received at the landing-place on disembarkation from the Oberon steamer by a guard of honour, consisting of British soldiers and Bashi-Bazouks.

> Thence they were conducted over the principal parts of the establishment, which were examined with less oriental apathy than usual. A collation was provided in the messroom, which had been decorated with French, Turkish, and British flags and wreaths formed of the shrubs growing around. The table was favoured moreover by the presence of nearly 30 ladies, both French and English, residents either in the Dardanelles or Renkioi, who had been invited for the occasion. The tout ensemble was picturesque. The dignified and solemn Turk sat at the same board with the simply dressed yet more lively

> and intelligent looking European. The French and British uniforms mingled with those of the Bashi-Bazouk officers who assembled in considerable numbers. When I add, that the ladies were almost without exception young and remarkable for their good looks, it may be readily imagined that the scene was one not often witnessed in Anatolia. The working men were not forgotten. They had their dinner followed by games in the evening, preceded by God save the Queen and long and loud continued cheering for Her Majesty. Three cheers were afterwards given for Dr Parkes, Mr Brunton and the ladies. A disturbance between the regular and irregular cavalry at Dardanelles, during which life has been lost, rendered it necessary that the Turkish dignitaries should depart sooner than was intended. We have not yet heard the result of the conflict.[15]

The hospital was lost in the Turkish countryside, and the principal relaxations were walks and picnics; the possession of a pony was an advantage for more distant forays. Ceramics were (and still are) a local industry, and pottery with designs based on ancient examples could be bought. On the northern side of the Dardanelles, British forces were mainly encamped at Gallipoli (now Gelibolu), and at Bulair (Bolayr), somewhat further north. Much nearer on the Asiatic side was Dardanelles (Çanakkale), which was the seat of local Turkish administration; the grand mansion owned by the Calverts dominated its waterfront. Opposite, on the European side, was the town now called Eceabat with Sestos a little to the north. Dr John Beddoe learnt Turkish and wrote in his reminiscences: 'Bosh is a word we have borrowed from the Turkish; it means emptiness, and thence nonsense. Thus "bosh lakirdie seuilersen" equals you speak empty words'.[16]

For much of the life of the hospital, the medical and nursing staff had too little rather than too much to occupy them, and the staff had time to pursue outside interests. Not required at once at Renkioi, Beddoe originally landed at Constantinople and set off to climb snowcapped Mount Olympus. This was much easier to reach from Scutari than from Renkioi. His party visited Brusa where there had been an earthquake. During the journey there were more earthquake tremors, and Christison injured his ankle and had to be carried on the back of a six-foot-four-inch companion.[17] After returning to Scutari they embarked for Renkioi. Dr Parkes, untrammelled by military red tape, was always ready to give short leave for a good purpose to any who were not really required.[18] Some travelled or visited the Crimea and others volunteered for service in the Crimea or at Scutari. Of those who remained at Renkioi over a long period, Beddoe and Eassie wrote accounts of life there. Beddoe showing his interest in ethnology, not only described himself (Chapter 6) but others. He began studying ethnology by recording the eye and hair colour of those he met, and there are frequent allusions to his companions' physical characteristics, Bader an athletic Swabian from the Black Forest, Stretton a well-made but delicate looking blond, and so forth. He contributed an addendum on ethnology to Dr Parkes' Report and, in later life, became Professor of Ethnology at Bristol. Kirk was already a botanist and was one of three medical authors of an 11-page botanical addendum to the Report.[19] In this they recorded 460 different plant species from 258 genera and were only unable to name 17. In April 1856, Kirk and Beddoe explored Mount Ida, where crimson, blue, and purple anemone carpeted the slopes,[20] and Beddow was delighted to identify A[nemone]. appenina. Repeatedly there are comments about the beauty of the wild flowers and the richness of the countryside.

Everyone in the campaign, from Lord Raglan downwards, was interested, from different viewpoints, in meteorology. Extensive weather records were kept at hospitals and were used to assess the healthiness of the area and to relate climatic conditions to specific illnesses. At Renkioi, William Robertson contributed an addendum on the subject to the Report. The climate was temperate but in mid-winter it was cold and wet, with the roads, always bad, turned into muddy tracks, and there was some snow. The hospital huts were warm but the houses of the Greek, and especially the Turkish workmen, were cold and woefully inadequate.[21] In summer it was dry and hot. At night jackals howled round the more isolated huts.

Kirk and Robertson were both keen amateur photographers. Kirk was interested in the building of the hospital, recording all the different stages of development, its environs and the local vegetation with fine studies of enormous Valonia oaks, while Robertson was mainly concerned with people, and documented the personnel at the hospital, officers and men from the Land Transport Corps (figure 14) stationed locally, Turks and 'Arabs', perhaps nomads, and some of the local Greek villagers. The minimum exposure was probably about three seconds, but even so, the images are remarkably sharp. Kirk's were salt prints or calotypes, and Robertson's albumen prints from collodion negatives. Photography had only existed for some fifteen years, and a great deal of skill must have been exercised; hot weather could make the work difficult. Parkes in a letter to Benjamin Hawes, wrote on 23 May 1855 that they had attempted to photograph 'a little ceremonial... when Mrs Calvert, the wife of the Consul attempted to drive in the first nail, but the collodion was not good'. However, other photographs and drawings were promised.[22]

The letters of Bransby Roberts, who was then in his early twenties, having qualified in 1853, give an insight into the minds of those working at Renkioi.[23] He had arrived on August 12 1855 by steamship, calling at Malta. Only 8 miles out of Malta, a pipe connecting the ship's engine and boiler had burst and the ship had limped along, passed at one point by a sailing ship. On arrival he had been amazed to discover that the hospital had no patients. He was also surprised that it was unfinished, and he found himself writing his letter in a vacant ward seated on a trunk at a table made from two iron bedsteads with three planks laid across. He expected to sleep on sacking with a railway rug over him and a hat box for a pillow. As it was a Sunday, the luggage would only be brought next day. The officers' quarters were still under construction, more inland but with a view of the sea. He was delighted by the beauty of the place, underlining the words real beauty, the blue sea, the beaches, and particularly the rim of hills behind the hospital. He had tried to see that his fiancée had a map of the area, but exactly the right one had not been bought by his father. However he believed she would spot the range of hills with a height of 1160 feet, and later named other places which he believed she would find. The little bay beside the rounded piece of land on which the hospital was standing was a refuge for shipping under all circumstances, enabling ships to load and unload with great facility. 'I view a long reach full of vessels of all descriptions backed by picturesque mountains'. Less attractive though were the mosquitoes and flies, and until the mess equipment was unpacked, he dismissed as trifles, water from a teacup, and soup taken with an iron spoon. He described Dr Parkes in these words: 'Dr Parkes appears to be a very nice man indeed - quite beyond my expectations'. He found the other doctors, some of whom he knew, 'very nice fellows' but feared that there might be some jealousy between the Scotch [sic] and English contingents.

Roberts spent much of his time on long walks, often when the weather was very hot. These reinforced his appreciation of the beauty of his surroundings which he compared with those at home. 'In many places, our walk had quite an English appearance, between hedgerows, in which are growing many very common English shrubs - plenty of wild convolvulus and mallows - there seems a profusion of wild flowers, even though most I hear have passed off.' This was in August. 'Altogether it is quite a medley – at one moment you go along a lane and all around you partake of home scenery, in another moment you come on fig trees & Greeks in full costume riding their ponies. I shall try and make a collection of the wild flowers for you if I can get a book to put them in and find they do not lose their colour completely which I am rather afraid they will and I have not forgotten the Ferns – none of which I have seen at the present time'.

Seen at a distance, the villages appeared delightful. The picturesque houses were built of stone in beautiful situations but, close to, he found them miserable and disgusting. Writing in October, he describes how 'the men having their shawls stuck full in front with pistols, "yataghan", sword etc, all very ancient looking and not formidable, they look very curious though – some of the men good looking but very few – the country is not nearly so unsettled as I expected, and we can all walk about very quietly.' A yatagan is a long Turkish dagger, without guard, usually curved.

In November, he and his party were invited into a Turkish home in one such village. They were given pipes and sat on a Turkish rug spread out in a rude shed. The little son of the owner, wearing a turban with flowers in it, brought them tea, passed round in a jar, but charcoal was also needed and the owner could not demean himself by jumping up and down to fetch it. His wife, inside the house, could not show herself but eventually curiosity overcame her and she opened the door a crack to throw the charcoal out. She was very plain but honest looking.

Close to the village were classical remains consisting of broken Greek and Roman pillars. He says, 'The Turkish village near which they are placed affords a fine contrast being composed of only six houses, some of which are partly built of the marble pillars in the neighbourhood. The remains prove how much this part of the country has degenerated and how much it might be improved under other masters and possibly under the present rule. All seems peacable [sic] enough but the inhabitants do not seem to have any desire beyond having just sufficient to eat and get tobacco.'

Before, during or after their stay at Renkioi, most of the staff visited Constantinople and, for those going to the Crimea, a stop there was usual. Constantinople was on the way to everywhere, with expatriates constantly bumping into those they had known before the war or during the campaign (as indeed also happened in the Crimea). Across the Bosphorus, the main military base was at Scutari, pleasant with broader streets, and reached usually by caique, sometimes in rough weather. Any visitor from Renkioi was coming to a capital city and a great port, the seat of the Turkish government, and of the legations of the great powers, the setting of constant diplomatic activity. The city was crowded, and there was plenty of scope for commercial enterprise, both on the part of the Turks and by British and foreign firms which were already in Turkey or arrived after the war started. The hamal, the reliable Turkish porter able to carry half the contents of a room on his back, astonished foreign visitors. The cart ordinarily used for conveying larger loads, the araba, consisted (in the words of Florence Nightingale), 'of loose poles and planks, extended between two axles – trees placed on small wheels, and drawn by a yolk of weak oxen'.[24] Tobacco was cheap, pipes were smoked everywhere, and the streets were thronged with people dressed 'in every imaginable costume – now a Turk, then a Greek, next a French lady in full Parisian costume, French officers, English and Sardinian ditto, English, French and Sardinian soldiers, a pasha on horseback with his train, a group of Turkish women, another of Greek ladies, a Greek priest in flowing robes, long beard, square cap; an Armenian priest in dark brown robes', and so forth.[25]

Constantinople, then with almost a million inhabitants, seen from afar, was a most beautiful city, encircled by water, in a superb setting. Crowded along the shores of the Bosphorus, were houses which often overhung the water, homes with terraced gardens, palaces, cemeteries, mosques, and minarets, and a particularly graceful palace belonging to the Sultan, painted in pale lilac, looking at a distance, as if it was resting on water.[26] Viewed more closely, the streets were poverty stricken and filthy; the houses which lined these narrow alleys were built of wood and under constant threat of fire. There were three principal districts. Stamboul was the old city, exclusively Turkish, with extensive Roman remains, such as the hippodrome and the great underground cistern, the great mosques, the Sultan's palace and the bazaar with streets of shops exclusively selling particular items such as fezzes or silk. Galata, the commercial sector with shipping warehouses, was said to be the worst and most filthy part of the city. Pera was the foreign and particularly French quarter. Further out were pleasant suburbs such as Therapia, its sea breezes a contrast to the scorching Scutari. In the bazaars and in shops, distinguished as Turkish by the lack of a name above the door, bargaining was invariable, possibly having become so with the influx of foreign visitors. The 'Honest Johnny' met the 'Honest Califty' and agreed a price. Unfortunately the meaning of califty is thief; in fact Turkish honesty was often favourably commented on.

In Pera and the European quarter were shops with the names of their English owners above them. An English bookshop existed, and shops and food stores selling necessities, sometimes exported from England, and delicacies, a far cry from Renkioi where, in its early days, necessities had continually to be borrowed by the more improvident. Near the Galata tower was Hanson and Co, the bank, in whose shaded waiting room could be read the English newspapers.[27] Scutari, reached by boat from Stamboul, was considered healthy. Streets there, round the hospitals, were renamed as reminders of home, for example, Albert Terrace and Wapping High Street.

Quarrels sometimes broke out, but underlying attitudes are best illustrated by a story, not from Constantinople but from Erenkioi, the village from which Renkioi Hospital got its name. There, Beddoe was inside a cafe when he heard an altercation outside, and when he ran out, found a naval officer from the fleet at Besika bay, being fended off by Beddoe's servant. The naval officer was attempting to forcibly remove, i.e. steal, Beddoe's horse. He excused himself by saying that, from its harness, he had thought it to be a Turkish horse. The officer seemed unaware that his conduct could invite criticism.[28]

Some went further than Constantinople. As soon as he arrived at Renkioi, Bransby Roberts was, like others, determined to visit the Crimea.[29] He was permitted to leave for the Crimea via Constantinople in the latter part of August, returning to Renkioi on September 4th. There were five in the party of which certainly four were doctors from Renkioi, and the fact that these could be spared, despite the expected arrival of patients, clearly indicates their lack of employment. The party included his closest friend, Samuel Stretton. They had the services of a local guide but only three horses so that Roberts and Stretton were on foot. All were overawed by the beauty of the Crimea, their senses heightened by their consciousness of war so that the scene, as they looked across the hills, seemed wholly unreal. Roberts had a good view of Sevastopol with its very strong fortifications, the 'wonderful Malakoff-Redan etc', and thought that Sevastopol looked pretty and anything but destroyed, with the sky clear and cloudless above, while off shore lay the allied squadron watching the harbour. Sevastopol seemed a small place to resist so large an attacking force. There was 'an occasional puff of white smoke and then the report but it was very difficult to realise that each gun was loaded and each puff of smoke indicated that some huge ball of iron was projected with the hope and intention of either killing someone or doing some other injury'. They were visiting as tourists, as many others had done before them. They came closer to the war when Roberts saw cannon balls lying on the ground but much closer when their guide warned them, in the neighbourhood of Inkerman, that the Russians were in the habit of shelling the ravines that they were negotiating. As the Relief Guard marched down the ravine below them, they heard the whizz of Russian shells and one fell 'quite as near as was agreeable'. After dark, 'flashes of musquetry sparkled and glittered, more like so many fire flies than anything else, and then a more livid light would arise as the hand grenades were thrown', for the Russians and French were so close that this was the favourite missile. No doubt Roberts and his companions must have wondered that, if their own circumstances changed, this would prove a preparation for the real thing. Roberts did not forget that two miles away the most memorable siege in the world was going on and that 'some 500,000 men were pitted against each other, moreover that not so many days before 4000 men had been sacrificed to this, I might call it demon War'. Roberts was referring to the Chernaia battle which had been fought about a fortnight before, between the Russians and the French and Sardinians, with heavy casualties on the Russian side. He was now gazing upon the end of the siege of Sevastopol, about a week before its fall on September 8th. In that final assault the casualties were far greater, with the Russians losing 13,000, and the allies 10,000 men.[30]

In all, Roberts and his party were in the Crimea for just over 48 hours. He talked of hoping to see friends, presumably other doctors, but time was too short to allow this. The various sights he saw gave him an impression of the battlefield, and he picked up a shell fragment and three bullets as mementos, but the true nature of war must have still been only in his imagination.

He returned to Renkioi with an injury to his wrist due to a fall which made writing painful and he makes very few further references to the real war. He mentions that the arrival of casualties is forecast, a possible posting for him to Abydos to look after 'convalescents' drafted from Renkioi, with the disagreeable prospect of no Mess, petty expenses, and 'dreadfully dull'. His letters give the impression of a young doctor, far away from England and entirely untrained in military matters. Other Civil Surgeons did volunteer to work in military hospitals and, of course, had the same active experience as their army colleagues.

On arrival, Roberts had believed that he would stay at Renkioi for some months, and in his second letter dated September 4th 1855 he says that his senior colleague, Henry Goodeve, conjectured that they might return home in June. In fact, Roberts was only at Renkioi for five months and was invalided home on 26 Jan 1856. He sailed on the transport Saldanha, the *Times* stating that 'he had never been in good health'[31], while Parkes supplied the diagnosis of rheumatic fever. On return to England, Bransby Roberts married Milly and spent a successful life as a general practitioner in Eastbourne. His obituary, in 1919, in describing his Crimean War experience, stated that he was assistant surgeon at Renkioi Hospital, Dardanelles, and was in camp before Sevastopol three days before its fall.[32]

Another account of a shorter stay at Renkioi, then service in the Crimea, is given by George Buchanan. He answered the call for volunteer civil surgeons in May 1855 and was at once accepted for Renkioi by Sir James Clark.[33] He was allowed to make his way to Renkioi by any route he chose as the hospital was not yet complete. He made a leisurely journey by way of the north of Italy, the Adriatic, the Gulf of Corinth, Greece, and Smyrna, finally arriving at Constantinople. From there he visited the Crimea, with the permission of his superiors, and stayed about a week. He then returned to Constantinople on a ship which had been carrying cattle. The flies were so thick that a white tablecloth was absolutely invisible with a moving mass of black, or rather blue, dots which had to be driven off if he tried to cut a piece of ham. On arrival at Scutari, he found that Lord Paulet, the commanding officer at the hospital, had 'no good name among the civilian staff', and he decided not to seek the quarters which could have been allotted. Instead he was put up in a rented Turkish house with medical colleagues including the pathologist, Dr William Aitken. By this time he had a fever ('Crimean Fever' as it was termed, the same term as that used for Florence Nightingale's illness when she visited the Crimea). He received sick rations, chicken soup, fine bread, three bottles of soda water, and two pounds of ice per day, being looked after by Dr Barr whose little children also visited him. He then stayed in the house of a friend at Therapia, a suburb of Constantinople, until fit enough to travel to Renkioi. During his convalescence, a band played nearby; periodically its volume rose to drown the cries of some poor wretch enduring the bastinado in a neighbouring Turkish prison. He visited Scutari and saw Florence

Nightingale, who was going about the wards and tending the sick like the ordinary attendants. She was wearing a black dress and chequered shawl and an old, large, scooped, straw bonnet, trimmed with black. A little earlier another visitor, a surgeon, described her as being of a staid and most lady-like deportment, serious, thoughtful, slender and about 30. The soldiers adored her.[34] Both impressions are so different from those given by photographs taken in her old age. Buchanan's account is that of a traveller, not a tourist, written for his friends and published much later, quite different from the letters that Roberts sent to his fiancée, which particularly described his own feelings, hopes and expectations, and the beauty of the country side. Buchanan concentrated on his journey and on his compatriots, and it is clear that he felt at home in a group of like-minded civil surgeons, not in much contact with the regular army doctors.

From Constantinople, he travelled to Renkioi on a very overcrowded French steamer, allowed on board by the shipping clerk, though he only possessed his British passport and not the Turkish firman and French passport that he also required. With him was George Macleod on his way to Smyrna. He arrived at Dardanelles (Çanakkale), found two of his future colleagues waiting with ponies to greet him, and set off for Renkioi, several miles away, along the beach, strewn with sponges. Himself and Dr Cowan were in the lead, next, his servant to be, Gibson, who was given the task of controlling two ponies without riders, and, bringing up the rear, Dr Maunder, armed with a long whip so that he could touch the unmounted ponies if necessary. Despite or possibly because of this precaution, on turning inland along paths just wide enough for a horse, the two unmounted ponies escaped, and, with difficulty, had to be recaptured.

After arrival at the hospital, he found he had no medical work to do and scarcely became acquainted with any of the staff. He visited Erenkioi, which he remarked on as a village of no note and occupied by Greeks of an inferior sort. He did not really approve of the rites of the Greek Orthodox Church, such a change from Presbyterianism. He had already witnessed difficulties over ritual at Therapia, when the position of the popular nonconformist chaplain had been threatened by the unexpected arrival of the regular chaplain from Scutari, a feud which needed to be diplomatically solved by Admiral Grey, the Senior Naval officer.

Buchanan only stayed at Renkioi for about ten days, as a message was received from Dr Hall, the Inspector General, calling for volunteers at the Camp General Hospital in the Crimea where, through illness, there was a serious shortage of medical staff. On September 8th (the same day as the Redan was taken), Cowan, Maunder, and he set off for the Crimea at 5.0 a.m. Buchanan did not introduce medical details into his account, as being unsuitable for his readers, but Maunder's medical adventures on arrival at the Crimea have been described in Chapter 5. They arrived at Dardanelles at 7.0 a.m. and boarded the Austrian Lloyd's steamer, Archduko Ludovici, at 2.0 p.m. There was a terrible crush of 'filthy Turks' on board, blocking the gangway, and they made their way up the paddle boxes, hauling up their own luggage. The steamer cast anchor in the Golden Horn at 2.0 p.m. the following day. Engaging a small boat, they went ashore, getting themselves and their luggage out through the cabin windows at the stern of the steamer.

In Constantinople there were no delays about securing their passage to the Crimea and, three days later, at 4.0 p.m. on September 12th, they embarked on the steamer Indian. Their ship passed another coming from the Crimea and within hailing distance. 'What news?' 'Sebastopol taken'. 'Is the North side taken?' 'No, but not a Russian to be seen.' Then they cheered. Their ship was off Balaklava on the 14th and they went ashore in the Captain's boat next day. With the help of Mr Jenner the purveyor, who had been at Renkioi, they managed to secure a small mule cart and, passing Mary Seacole's establishment, reached the Camp General Hospital. Buchanan presented his credentials to Dr Hall and he was appointed to the General Hospital.

Buchanan's experiences differed from those of Roberts. Buchanan's first glimpse of the real war in which he was playing a part was of the Redan which he entered a week after it had fallen and from there he went into Sevastopol itself. There were still occasional Russian shells so that it was not wise to linger. He admired the defences devised by Tolbeden and the gun emplacement with their individual walls protecting individual gun crews but he was horrified at the piles of putrefying dead crammed into the ditch, immediately as he entered the Redan, and then by the sight of the dead still lying everywhere in the huge Russian hospital. Buchanan's duties in the Crimea did not last very long for he received a letter from his father asking that he should return home to look after his father's practice. His father had a severe attack of rheumatism and was quite disabled. He decided to return, and Dr Hall agreed quite readily. Eighteen hours after receiving the request he was on the Bahania. On the voyage home, when the ship passed Renkioi he could see the tin roofs of the hospital glittering in the sunshine. After a short delay in Malta, he embarked on a P&O steamer and returned via Marseilles and overland through France. Leaving Marseilles on November 2nd, he took advantage of the 'Crimean Heroes' half price fare and, after a day sight-seeing in Paris, was having a long chat on the 5th with Sir James Clark about affairs in the East. Thus ended six months as a civil surgeon.

At Smyrna in July 1855, it became dangerous for Europeans to leave the town, and a local medical practitioner, Dr McCraith, was held captive by local brigands. He was released unharmed on payment of a ransom.[35] At Renkioi, a unit of the Turkish army, the Bashi-Bazouks, became a source of anxiety. The Turkish army was a large and effective fighting force engaged during the Crimean war in campaigns around the Danube, in the Crimea, at Kars, and in Asiatic Turkey. Within the army was a unit of Turkish Irregulars or Osmanli Horse, commonly known as the Bashi-Bazouks [translated: broken-heads]. They were notorious in British circles for their ill-discipline; indeed their own officers could not control them. They were stationed fairly close by, the only direct contact Renkioi would have had with Turkish forces, and were often almost regarded as foes rather than friends or allies. Roberts referred to them in one of his letters, avoiding so far as possible anything that would alarm Milly.

The *Times* Correspondent writing on September 28 1855 said:

> I see that the character of that irregular force, the Bashi-Bazouks, is occupying some share of public attention. Their encampment being only 10 miles from Renkioi Hospital, we enjoy occasional opportunities of studying their habits and hear frequent reports of their proceedings. A favourite pastime of theirs consisted in riding ventre a terre, and fully armed, through the narrow, and now usually crowded streets of the Dardanelles, or Tcheni-Kalesi, while expostulation was regarded as an insult, to be avenged on the spot by the pistol or dagger. A party of them lately fired upon some French soldiers upon very slight provocation, and an enquiry was instituted, but although the matter was allowed by our allies to pass, I heard that the French had good grounds for complaint, and that the conduct of the 'irregulars' was most violent. One passes over the men as a set of demi-savages, whose courage, skill in horsemanship, and dexterity in the

> use of their weapons have been lauded quite as much as is deserved. We make up our minds to be pestered with them sometimes on our rides, as was a young naval officer the other day, who, upon returning by the seashore from an excursion on horseback rather late, found himself suddenly side by side with a 'Bashi' who held a pistol at his head. My friend in a second had his revolver at the fellow, who upon seeing the officer armed attempted to fly; but the other got hold of him, dragged him from his horse, and treated him very roughly before the brigand could manage to escape.[36]

Brunton records that one evening he saw a column of cavalry approaching. The men were laden with sheep, fowls, geese, grain etc, stolen from farms where some farmers had been murdered. He immediately took active measures for the safety of the hospital, informing the British and Turkish authorities, arranging defence, which included firing at the advancing columns, and having women and children taken off to two ships which had, that day, brought reinforcements The Bashi-Bazouks left, and, according to Brunton, were later nearly all killed. Brunton's own wife and son arrived as the incident finished.

The *Times* in the dispatch dated September 28th refers to this event as having taken place in July, the Bashi-Bazouks being 130 deserters who shouted, 'English! no bono' as they approached. They then rode up to the village of Erenkioi with the intention of ransacking Frederick Calvert's house there but were diverted and later went on to the plain of Troy to plunder his farm at Thymbra. Two of the marauders returned to the farm after the band had ridden off, got well beaten by his servants, and one became a patient at the hospital. Thirty or forty of the deserters then rode into the Hospital encampment and were received as Brunton described. Brunton's account for his grandchildren was straightforward. Once again he described himself playing the central role, in exciting terms, sending to the Consul (Frederick Calvert) for help, arming the staff as best he could, the arrival of a paddle steamer with three or four companies of Turkish soldiers, and arranging for an East Indiaman, standing off shore, to send ashore men, two cannonades, firearms and ammunition. Later it was discovered that the Turkish soldiers, sent as a protection, had stolen the lead for making bullets with which he had supplied them. The situation was resolved when a British garrison arrived.[37]

A later copy of the *Times*, clearly referring to the same incident, records that not many weeks before, Calvert's farm at Thymbra, some six miles from the hospital, had been surrounded by 100-200 Bashi-Bazouks deserters. After the farm had been pillaged for some time they were fired on and 'three of the brigands lie buried here'.[38]

The *Times* correspondent had first hand experience himself. His door 'which happened to have no lock was one night pushed open by a Bashi "in his cups" with a gun in his hand and a stomach full of pistols; he held a pretty bay horse by the bridle. I could not persuade him that he had lost his way; he demanded 'monish' as he termed the British coin – in a very impressive manner.' The arrival of the correspondent's friend induced him to withdraw. Sentries were then placed beyond the lines of the buildings, the nocturnal interruptions ceased, and the countryside became peaceful enough for ladies 'to ride about freely and as late as in an English county'.

Amongst the officers of the Bashi-Bazouks stationed in the vicinity was Captain Richard Burton, later famous as explorer and scholar. He had brought a number of Afghan horsemen across Persia and Anatolia. Beddoe, who met him, surmised later that it was this experience which suggested to him that he should pass as an Ethiopian on his famous pilgrimage to Mecca.[39] At the time, Burton was involved in a ridiculous incident when his commanding officer, General Beatson, in command of irregulars originally known as Beatson's Horse, was considered to have incited mutiny amongst his own troops. Burton, according to War Office records, was thought to have encouraged Beatson and was considered small fry, and 'cut out as a firebrand'.[40]

Another account is by William Eassie, the Assistant Engineer who was at Renkioi as long as anyone, from May 1855 to August 1856. He visited Constantinople and Smyrna and wrote his recollections of Renkioi very soon after returning to England, using the pseudonym Rattlebrain. The book, entitled *Romaic Beauties and Trojan Humbugs*, is written, in keeping with the pseudonym, in a rather jocular style but is a detailed description of Renkioi from a different viewpoint to that of the doctors.[41] Eassie did not write of professional matters, never referred to British patients, or indeed to Brunton, his superior, or to Parkes, and made no allusion to the war. He knew his own workforce well and set out to find out all he could about those he met and the land they and he were living in. Interested in distinguishing the various races of the local inhabitants, he paid rather more attention to the ladies than to the men. He saw the former in a chivalrous and romantic light and in his book, written at the age of 23, there was no Milly (of Roberts' letters) mentioned or anyone like her. More light-heartedly, in 1864, he wrote a further book under the same pseudonym.[42] This was 182 pages of poetry with illustrations by Phiz, who was a friend of his father, and describes how a Briton (named Straggler) 'drilled for his fatherland, won an heiress, and caught the rheumatism'.

He enjoyed describing a Greek wedding with the elaborate headdress, clothes, and make up of the bride, and the 'gently constellating beauty' of Osmanli (Ottoman) women. The bride had to keep her eyes closed for a period of several hours during the marriage feasting and ceremony, which Eassie recounted in detail. He described the Greek face as one 'which will last for ever' and goes on: 'The brow of Jupiter, the eyes of Niobe, the chin of Diana, the lips of Aphrodite, as chased by the chisels of old Greece, shall never wholly pass away'.[43] In Mysia (the Eastern margin of the Troad) the Greek maidens were very shy. Girls and young married women marked their faces with black patches, using juice from the broken stalk of a flower; this juice was also used to lengthen the eyebrow. Elaborate necklaces and the florio-zebbero, a band of small gold coins, usually worn round the forehead as a border to the fez, fascinated him. However he concluded by saying that 'there is little or no poetry in these Romaic maidens beyond that which emanates from their looks and movements. They resemble cylinders bossed on the outside with rarest taste, but with an interior full of a kind of blister and corrosion...' and then, changing the metaphor, 'they are ingot bars of true gold; but not the auriferous metal worked up by education and feeling into an inestimable filigree'.

Eassie travelled widely and accepted Turkish hospitality, and seemed most at home when in the company of Beddoe and Kirk. He enjoyed going to local ceremonies and spoke some Turkish. In the Smyrna bazaar he saw beautifully dressed dolls, the folded cloths of which opened like a painter's book of gold leaf and on these Lilliput forms could be studied every aspect of harem furniture in miniature from the kaltsa thetis, or garden, to the phonta metaxa, or fig tassel. He spent the night in Turkish tents with sometimes, as his companions, two dozen lizards, thousands of ants, black centipedes, hairy yellow tarantulas, scorpions, and snakes, acquiring, for good measure, 20 or 30 mosquito bites.

Anything connected with his work always interested Eassie, who compared plaster and the like with their British equivalents. Local customs sometimes surprised or dismayed him. Turkish workmen, digging a well at the hospital, made a large hole, throwing the soil out on to the ground, then digging out the next section of slightly smaller bore, putting the soil on the platform at the top of this narrower section, and then repeating the procedure until the right depth was reached. The whole, seen in section, was reminiscent of a telescope. He wrung his hands when he watched the indigenous Turkoman gipsies, whom he described as sons of the forest and mountain,[44] using only old saws made from scrap metal, instead of modern saws powered by water, water power that, alas, simply went to waste. Once he was involved in a hold-up but extricated himself by threatening the bandit with the vengeance of the local pasha.

The doctors' reminiscences are revealing but less is known about the experiences of less well educated staff. Among this staff were Ann Newman, a nurse, and Frank Day / Death, an orderly who were married two months after leaving Renkioi.[45]

Perhaps Holmes Coote revealed what the junior medical staff generally felt about life at Renkioi when he wrote later, 'the medical staff were all paid, and being isolated from the outer world could turn their attention to elegant pursuits. Life in it was perfect and calm. A wandering Bashi-Bazouk, a shower of rain or a flight of wild ducks threw a whole encampment into a flutter of surprise. The life was pleasant but with something of a tameness in it'.[46] No doubt hunting boars with a revolver, another pursuit, provided contrasting, if less elegant, excitement. For some, Renkioi provided another different excitement, as the next chapter shows.

[1] *Times* 19 Feb 1856. It is not known which correspondents were responsible for reports about Renkioi but the description of the work of the hospital and the surrounding scenery was always enthusiastic.

[2] *Times* 25 Dec 1855.

[3] *Times* 20 Oct 1855.

[4] *Times* 20 Oct 1855.

[5] TNA WO 43/91.

[6] *The History of the Times Vol II 1841-1884.* 178, 574. London: *The Times*, 1939.

[7] Buchanan G *Camp Life as seen by a Civilian. A personal narrative.* 165. Glasgow: James Macclehouse, 1871.

[8] Clapham J. Ed. *John Brunton's Book.* 60. Cambridge: Cambridge University Press, 1939
[9] Bransby Roberts. Letters. Copies of four letters are in the National Army Museum, the remainder in a private collection.
[10] Rattlebrain (William Eassie). *Romaic Beauties and Trojan Humbugs*. London. William Tweedie, 1858.
[11] *Times* 25 Dec 1855.
[12] *Times* 25 Dec 1855.
[13] *Times* 25 Dec 1855.
[14] Shepherd J. *The Crimean War Doctors* 2. 443 Liverpool: University Press. Liverpool, 1991.
[15] *Times* 10 Oct 1855.
[16] Beddoe J. *Memories of eighty years*. 75. Bristol: Arrowsmith, 1910.
[17] Beddoe J. *Memories of eighty years*. 67. Bristol: Arrowsmith, 1910.
[18] Beddoe J. *Memories of eighty years*. 80. Bristol: Arrowsmith, 1910.
[19] Parkes EA. *Report on the Formation and General Management of Renkioi Hospital on the Dardarnelles*, Turkey. 51-64. London :War Department, 1857.
[20] Beddoe J. *Memories of eighty years*. 109 Bristol: Arrowsmith, 1910.
[21] *Times* 29 Nov 1855.
[22] TNA WO 43/ 991.
[23] Bransby Roberts Letters.
[24] Cook ET. *The Life of Florence Nightingale* 1.203 London: Macmillan 1913.
[25] *A Lady Volunteer. Eastern Hospitals and English Nurses*. 1.305 .London: Hurst and Blackett. 1856.
[26] *A Lady Volunteer. Eastern Hospitals and English Nurses*. 1.294. London: Hurst and Blackett. 1856.
[27] Buchanan G. *Camp Life as seen by a Civilian. A personal narrative.* 25. Glasgow: James Macclehouse 1871.
[28] Beddoe J. *Memories of eighty years*. 110. London: Arrowsmith, 1911.
[29] Bransby Roberts B. Letters.
[30] Royle T. *Crimea. The Great Crimean War 1854-1856*. 414. London: Little, Brown & Co., 1999.
[31] *Times* 19 Feb 1856.
[32] *Medical News. Lancet* 1919. 1.688.
[33] Buchanan G. *Camp Life as seen by a Civilian. A personal narrative.* 295. Glasgow: James Macclehouse, 1871.
[34] *Medical Intelligence. Glasgow Medical Journal* 1856; 3. 365.
[35] *Medical Times & Gazette* 1855; 11. 25.
[36] *Times* 20 Oct 1855.
[37] Clapham J. Ed. *John Brunton's Book.* 63-67. Cambridge: Cambridge University Press, 1939.
[38] *Times* 7 Nov 1855.

[39] Beddoe J. *Memories of eighty years* 75. Bristol: Arrowsmith, 1910.
[40] TNA WO 32/ 7515.
[41] Rattlebrain (William Eassie) *Romaic Beauties and Trojan Humbugs.* London: William Tweedie, 1858.
[42] Rattlebrain (William Eassie). *Sir Guy de Guy. A stirring Romaunt.* London: Routledge, Warne & Routledge, 1864.
[43] Rattlebrain (William Eassie). *Romaic Beauties and Trojan Humbugs* 15. London: William Tweedie, 1858.
[44] Rattlebrain (William Eassie). *Romaic Beauties and Trojan Humbugs.* 63. London: William Tweedie, 1858.
[45] Web http.www.dorsetbay.plus.com/source/crimeadetail
[46] Coote H. *Hospitalism. British Medical Journal*; 1869. 1. 565-566.

Figure 15: Kemer Aqueduct, 1855.
Photograph by Dr. Kirk and originally published in Studia Troica 2004.
Probably the first photograph taken of the aqueduct.

Chapter 9

Renkioi and the Classical World

'The land of magic tales of long ago'.
Many a Time, Clement Attlee

Renkioi Hospital was built on the northern edge of the region in Asiatic Turkey (known as the Troad),[1] which was believed to have been under Trojan rule. The site of ancient Troy was then thought most likely to be at Bunarbashi (now Pinarbasi) near the Calverts' Thymbra farm (Figure 16a). Bunarbashi was about sixteen miles (26 km.) from the hospital, while Hisarlik, now considered the site of Troy, was nearer, some ten miles (16 km.) away (Figure 16b). Between the nearby hills behind Renkioi and the Sigeum ridge, the Scamander river, true to its alternative name of Meander, follows a leisurely course. East of Renkioi along the Dardanelles, is another famous link with great antiquity, the narrows known as the Hellespont. There, graphically described by Herodotus, a bridge, built on boats, allowed the Persian army under Xerxes to cross the Hellespont. Later in 334 BC, it was crossed again by Alexander the Great. Emulating Byron who swam the Hellespont in 1810, Doctors Bader and Armitage, accompanied by a boat, accomplished the distance of two nautical miles in June 1855 in an hour and eight minutes, in a disagreeably choppy sea while four steamers and eleven sailing ships passed them. One of these two gentlemen was for some time detained in a fishing net.[2]

Far away, one great supporter of classical education, Mr Gladstone, busied himself in the Welsh hills, as Sevastopol fell, with Homer and Homeric literature.[3] That the Trojan War took place and was historic rather than mythical was then (as now) yet to be established, but since Schliemann's excavations there, commenced in 1870, Hisarlik has been generally accepted as the site of Troy.

Within a radius of twenty miles of the Hospital are many reminders of the Ancient World. They include the quarry and prostrate columns at Koceli made for a building order which was never completed, the scattered remains of Alexandria Troas where a similar column lies on the sea shore and the Kemer aqueduct, photographed by Dr Kirk (Figure 15).

Everywhere are archaeological sites, some despoiled to provide material for later buildings and even balls for Turkish cannon, and some by earthquakes. Parkes wrote in his Report:

> Placed as we were at Renkioi, on the borders of the Plain of Troy, and in the vicinity of the ruins of so many cities which were great and flourishing before or in the days of the lower Empire, it was the intention of several of the officers of the hospital to devote some of the time to a systematic investigation of the remains of antiquity which were so profusely scattered about. But the speedy termination of the war prevented these intentions being carried out, and the only investigations of consequence were made by Mr Brunton after the hospital works had been stopped. A few objects found in the cemeteries of ancient Dardanos, and in the cemetery of unknown age, supposed to be near the site of old Troy, and among the more modern ruins of Novum Ilium, have been brought home by Mr Brunton, and presented to the British Museum.[4]

Parkes made this reference to John Brunton, but did not realise the significance of one of his activities for Renkioi Hospital was to add something to archaeological history. Surprisingly, this contribution was made, not by the doctors who by then were returning to Britain, but by Brunton and Eassie, the engineers. They separately described the first excavation made at what is now accepted as the true site of Troy. Brunton's account was in his *Book*,[5] and Eassie's in *Romaic Beauties and Trojan Humbugs*.[6] Brunton's *Book* was revealed when it was published in 1939 long after his death. Eassie's account had been completely forgotten and came to light during my own studies.[7] The words 'Trojan Humbugs' allude to Troy and the ideas that surrounded it.

In July 1856, when the hospital was being dismantled, Brunton conducted excavations at two sites, first at Hanay Tepe, 500 yards from the Calvert farm at Thymbra, and secondly at Hisarlik, Ilium Novum. The two sites were about seven miles (11 km) apart. William Eassie already knew the site for he makes reference to observations made in the previous year, 1855[8]. Brunton took 150 of his 'army works corps fellows', and fearing, that with nothing to do they might get into mischief, he first 'camped them on the plains of Troy'. When referring to Troy, it is likely that Brunton was speaking of Bunarbashi, then considered the site of Troy. He first engaged his work force in excavations at a site he termed the 'Necropolis'. This will have been at Hanay Tepe, considered at the time to have been Troy's burial ground.[9] Brunton continues, 'my men did not like this at first, but an extra pint of stout per day which I ordered for them partly reconciled them to it. They found 'ancient tombs, sarcophagi, amphorae, vases, armlets, anklets, ear-rings etc.' or as Eassie put it, 'urns, statuettes, pottery and pithoi'. They now worked with zeal and some were next detached to Ilium Novum. The detachment then conducted excavations on this second site at the Graeco-Roman town of Ilium Novum including the mound at Hisarlik, the site subsequently identified by Schliemann as ancient Troy. So Brunton's excavations in 1856, though not in any way formal, and made 14 years before the excavations of Schliemann, can be taken as the first excavations at the true site. (See maps overleaf).

At Hisarlik, Brunton's account of the findings is as follows: they found the ruins of a temple including the capital of a Corinthian column, shaken down in an earthquake. As it weighed over three tons it was left there. Nearby the walls of a house were found and a tessellated pavement with, at its centre, an oval depiction of a boar hunt beautifully worked in various tinted marbles. Before he could cut it out he received messages from the hospital which forced him and his men to return at once. He left the pavement covered but on his return a fortnight later the mosaic had been removed. Later he heard that it had already been placed below the altar in the floor of a Greek church but it would now be as much as the priest's life was worth to remove it.[10] It was next reported to be in a church at Kalafat but this church no longer exists.

Brunton's part in these investigations was very important. However Eassie, his assistant, may well have encouraged Brunton to excavate. Brunton was educated in small private schools, and for two sessions studied mathematics, French, and Latin at London University, before becoming a pupil in an engineering firm at Hayle, Cornwall[11]. Apart from the excavations at Hisarlik his diary contains no references to archaeology and there is no other evidence that it interested him though he made sure that his finds

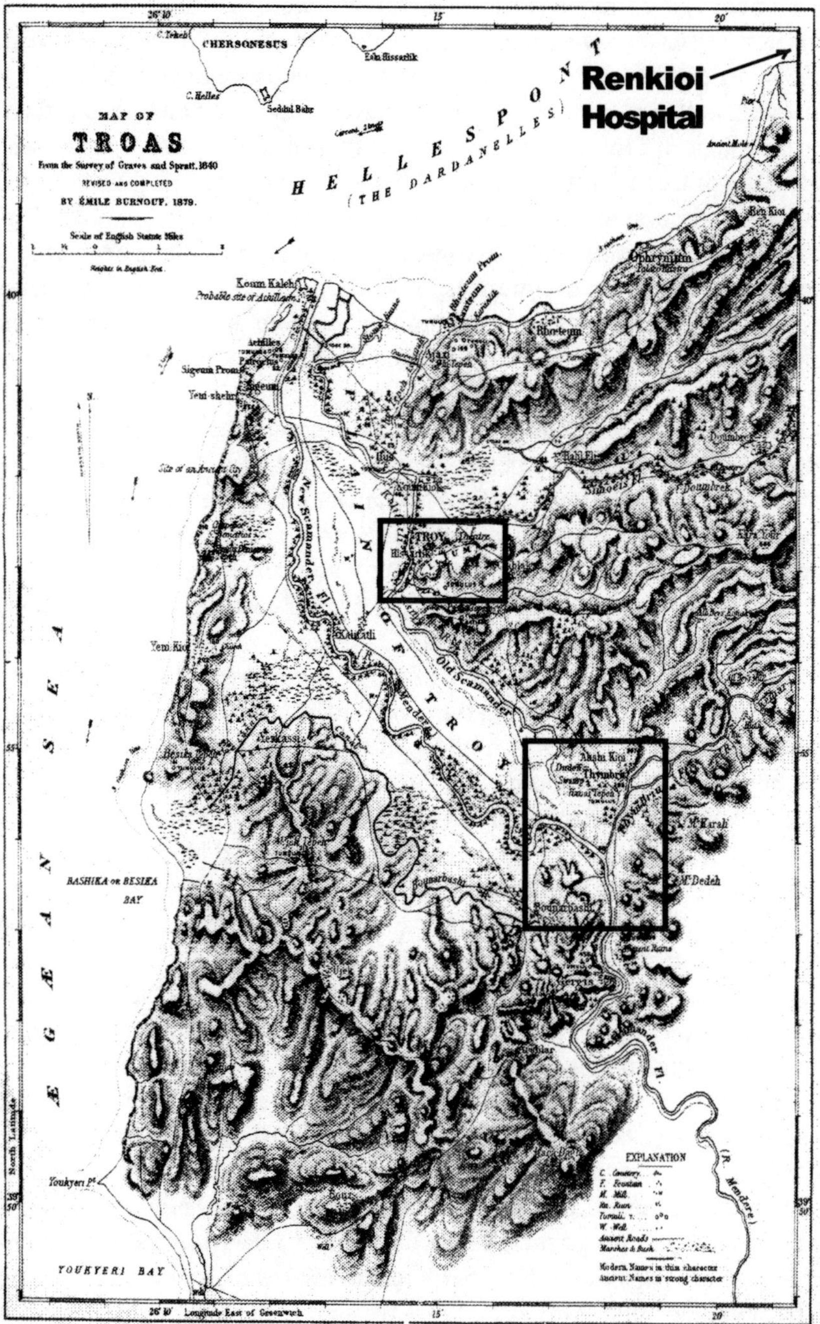
MAP OF
TROAS
From the Survey of Graves and Spratt, 1840
REVISED AND COMPLETED
BY ÉMILE BURNOUF, 1879.
Scale of English Statute Miles
Heights in English Feet.
Renkioi
Hospital
CHERSONESUS
C. Helles
Seddul Bahr
HELLESPONT
(THE DARDANELLES)
Koum Kaleh
Probable site of Achilleum
Sigeum Prom.
Yeni-shehr
Rhoeteum
Ophrynium
TROY
Old Scamander
New Scamander
PLAIN OF TROY
Simoeis Fl.
Yeni Kioi
Thymbra
Bounarbashi
BASHIKA or BESIKA BAY
ÆGEAN SEA
YOUKYERI BAY
Youkyeri Pt.
EXPLANATION
Modern Names in thin character
Ancient Names in strong character
(R. Mendere)
Longitude East of Greenwich
North Latitude

Figure16a (left): All maps of the area were based on the survey carried out in 1840 by Lieutenant (later Vice-Admiral) Spratt RN and published as Admiralty Chart 1608 in 1844. A version of this survey is illustrated left. This was used by Schliemann in his 'Ilios' published in 1870. Renkioi Hospital lay just outside the margin of this map, and is indicated by an arrow. The areas where the party from Renkioi conducted their excavations were at Thymbra Farm and then at Hisarlik. These are highlighted. Close to Thymbra Farm lay the village of Bunarbashi , now called Pinarbasi, which was then thought of as the likely site of Ancient Troy (Figure 16c). At the second site, marked Troy, was the mound of Hisarlik which is now accepted as the site of Ancient Troy (Figure 16b). Figures 16b and 16c are more detailed views of these highlighted sites.

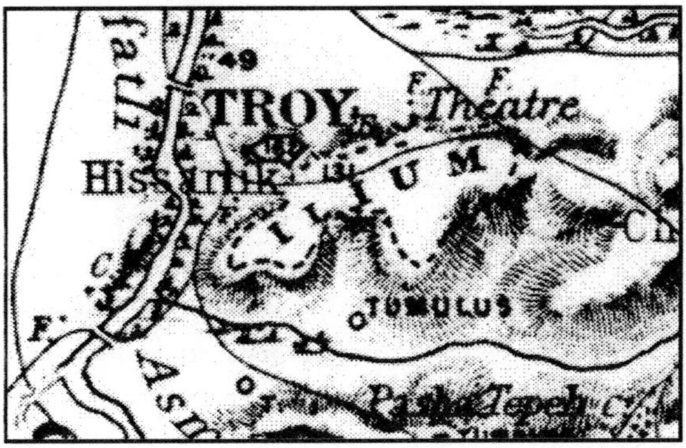

Figure 16b (above): Troy showing the site of Ilion or Ilium Novum, the Graeco-Roman town built later, with, at its north west corner, Hisarlik, the site of Ancient Troy. Detail from an 1894 version of Spratt's map.

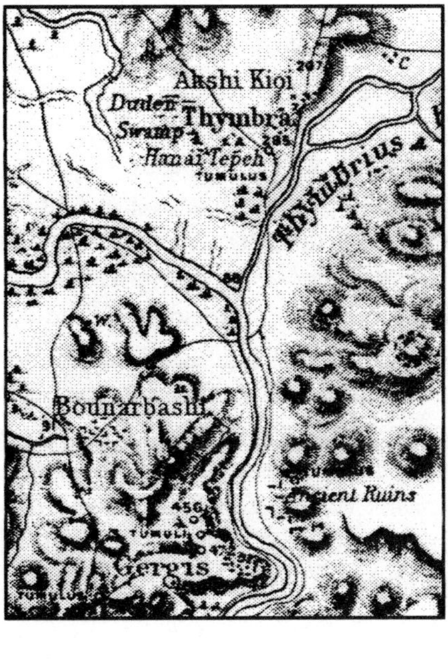

Figure 16c (right): Enlarged view of the area round Thymbra Farm and including the village of Bunarbashi.

were reported to the British Museum. Eassie as a child lived in Dundee, and almost certainly attended a leading school there, though lists of pupils no longer exist.[12] His family then moved to Gloucester where his father built up the firm which supplied many of the wooden huts being manufactured for the army. There, Eassie Junior trained as an engineer, training probably useful in practical archaeology. When at Renkioi he certainly conducted excavations himself, speaking of digging trenches to circumvallate an object and percussing the ground with a crowbar 'until you light upon a spot which emits a hollow or bosse [bump] sound upon being struck'.[13] His account of the excavations at Hisarlik is much more complete than Brunton's cursory description, and he had a greater interest in Classical matters than most of the others at Renkioi.[14]

Brunton and Eassie did not dig by chance at Hisarlik, which was on land owned by Frederick Calvert. For those at Renkioi, the Calvert brothers were local mentors; Brunton's choice of where to dig must have depended on them. Frederick Calvert, the dynamic elder brother and British consul, was greatly interested in archaeology, and his home was the staging post for many visitors with archaeological interests. There, in the house and garden, classical remains were on view. His less thrusting younger brother, Frank, was an expert self-taught archaeologist with a great knowledge of the Troad, whose reputation has grown with time. Eassie mentions very appreciatively the Calverts' open hospitality, and he and Frank Calvert visited sites together. It was to be Frank Calvert who directed Schliemann to dig at Hisarlik, help that Schliemann later came to deny.[15]

In his book, *Romaic Beauties and Trojan Humbugs*, Eassie wrote that 'the newest puzzle of these parts is the discovery of a large and ancient cemetery at Batak, near Atchekioi, or near Harman Tepe, and at the Callicone of some authors. The Consul's chiftik is built upon the hill above this cemetery, and upon this hill are still to be noticed the apparent ruins of a large city, but no very clear traces of a wall. Behind the hill, and at its foot rolls a considerable brook, and to the west of this, on the lower, but not however the lowest plain, lies the large cemetery'.[16]

Turning to Hisarlik, Eassie says that in the foundations of a temple 'in the uppermost flat of the Hissarjik hill' where he was expecting to find some Roman remains, he found instead a long piece of marble on which was inscribed in Greek (Figure 17a) what was seemingly a public memorial to the leader of the sacred heathen choruses, for his benevolence and goodness of disposition.[17] A second inscription in Greek (Figure 17b) was also found. One now appears to be in the Çanakkale Archaeological Museum and the other is recorded as having been found at Kalafat.[18]

(A) "ΟΔΗΜΟΣΟΜΗΘΥΜΝΑΙΟΝ
ΤΟΝΑΤ
ΟΝΤΑΡΑΛΟΝΚΑΤΑΟΣΝΑΡΕΤΗΣΙΝΕΡ
ΚΑΙΕΥΝΟΙΑΣΤΗΣΡΙΣΕΑΥΤΟΝ"

(B) " ΑΙΔΕΚΑΠΡΩΣΙΝΕΣΚΟΛΩ
ΙΕΥΧΑΡΙΣΤΟΥΤΕΙΜΗΣΤΟ "

Figures 17a ,17b: Inscriptions transcribed by William Eassie.

Translation is difficult due to faults in the characters, either produced by the original masons or by Eassie in transcription.

Both inscriptions are in Greek, the local language. Figure (a) is an honorific decree voted by the Mythymnaean people to an unknown honorand (possibly Attalos) because of his benefaction. If this inscription does refer to King Attalos, it presumably dates to a period in which Pergamum (and Mythymna) was not under Roman rule. Figure (b) is very fragmentary and probably concerned with dedication or taxes. I am indebted to Anne Wright for these expert comments.

In the vicinity of Ilium Novum, he also describes the wonderful mosaics, very elaborate pavements depicting lions, foxes, tigers, goats, and dogs of doubtful breed in full chase after a boar. These pavements had been riven, he assumed, by earthquakes. One very fine piece of work was a man on horseback contending with some strange parthana (sic) nondescript or other which he reckoned as fine as the great mosaics of Constantine. He also saw well cemented water pipes which varied not an inch in size from those which were currently being used locally. Eassie died in 1888 and Brunton in 1899. Their obituaries each stated, with no mention of the other, that each had been the first to excavate at the true site of Troy, long before Schliemann.

In neither Brunton's nor Eassie's account of the excavation is there any mention of the doctors. The exact date of Brunton's excavations is not known, but almost certainly they had already left for England, otherwise, with a classical education, they would have been interested in these activities. The breadth of their education was indicative of the learned profession which medicine had become. Latin was essential for entrants to English and Scottish medical schools. A letter to a medical journal could be signed with a pseudonym in Greek characters. As late as 1868, of 155 candidates for membership of the Royal College of Surgeons, 74 were rejected, 67 of these having failed in Latin.[19] At the Royal College of Physicians in London, the College lectures were delivered in English, apart from the most prestigious, the Harveian Oration, which was delivered in Latin until 1864. Then Robert Lee began the oration in Latin but was forced to conclude in English.[20]

Some doctors, usually on horseback and in a small party, with Eassie sometimes accompanying them, travelled widely to see archaeological sites. Beddoe visited the Greek and Roman remains at Assos, before later excavations were made. It was at Assos with its beautiful views that Dr Stretton spent a week, sleeping in 'native' houses and returning with three hundred flea bites on one hand. They noted thick Cyclopean walls in tolerably good condition at Chigii.[21] Chigii was Neandria, an identification suggested by Frank Calvert.[22] Beddoe remarked on the cairn, high on the hill, which had long borne the great name of 'Tomb of Hector'.[23] He noted too that: 'the barrow called the "tomb of Patroclus" near Yeni-Shehr (Sigeum) to the west of Mendereh, has been opened by some people from the fleet when it lay in Besika Bay before the war broke out. I cannot tell what they found there; but when we visited the spot I saw some bones which had not been carried away. They certainly had not belonged to the hero, but to a small and youthful person, probably female. I saw no signs of cremation'.

At Alexandria Troas, he saw a fine ruin, probably of baths, miscalled the palace of Priam.[24] 'Of course, wherever Troy may have been it was not there'. On his way to Alexandria Troas he 'had seen Yedi Tash (Seven Stones), which are huge monolithic columns, each fully thirty feet long, lying still in the ancient quarry at Kocali where they were hewn. Probably they were intended for erection at Alexandria Troas, but the coming of evil times caused their abandonment'[25] Pergamon would have required a fortnight's expedition, so had to be foregone.

Beddoe, remarking that it was generally thought that Bunarbashi was the site of Troy, says, 'Most of us visited Bunarbashi and examined the great springs'. Homer had told of the twin springs of Scamander, one hot with steam rising from it, the other ice cold even in summer.[26] This description perhaps fitted the Kirk Goz, or 40 eyes or springs, below the village. Beddoe measured the temperature of all 37 springs, the approximate number which other observers have found at this site. Like others he found that that they were tepid or cool, their temperature between 62-64 Fahrenheit. One spring had to be tested for him by a Turk, who was standing close at hand, because the Turk's harem was bathing there. Eassie, who accompanied Beddoe, was enchanted by a perfect garden of grass and flowers nearby, with innumerable camomile beds and also a great number of land tortoises.[27]

Twenty-four years later, in 1879, there was another visitor to the district, with similar interests. Rudolf Virchow, the great German pathologist, visited the springs and found, using an extremely accurate thermometer, that their temperatures varied but little. Virchow was visiting his great friend, Schliemann, and besides sharing Schliemann's archaeological interests, acted as the medical officer to his workers and to local people, for there were no doctors or apothecaries in the area. Some patients who were from Erenkioi, were so grateful that they gave him bouquets of flowers from their flower pots and terraces, when he passed through the village on his way to collect medicines from Dardanelles. To be fever free, villages in the Troad were on the hill tops. Virchow noticed much tertian malaria among those living on the plains.[28] Virchow also acted as scientist to the party and used his knowledge of botany to catalogue the rich variety of plants nearby, just as those at Renkioi had done.

From steep slopes above the Hospital, Eassie and the *Times* correspondent believed they looked down on an ancient mole running into the sea. Eassie said of the mole that, 'on a low shore a considerable mole ran out to sea. The offset ruins of this pier may still be seen.' This mole was noticed by Frank Calvert in 1853, when he investigated Ophrynium, the originally Greek settlement immediately overlooking the shelf of land on which the hospital stood. Charles Newton from the British Museum also saw the remains of an ancient mole when he stayed with the Calverts about the same time.[29] The account of Calvert's finds were recorded in the Archaeological Journal in 1860, using Brunton's map to illustrate the text.[30] A mole at the site of the harbour of Ophrynium appears on this map; this ancient mole had disappeared by the time the area was examined in the 1960s, and its existence was considered doubtful.[31] At Ophrynium, Eassie again indicated that his role in archaeology was active when he spoke of uncovering an ancient wall, no doubt using the Renkioi workforce and following Frank Calvert's advice.[32]

At Dardanos, to the north of the Hospital, Eassie found much more to interest him. He referred to excavations at the Necropolis where Greek workmen used only wooden spades when iron implements could easily have been obtained from a vessel nearby. He also noticed English workmen, digging on their own account with practically no permission required. They uncovered a peculiar leaden box with indented sides, subsequently altered into a tobacco pouch.[33]

Cremation had been common, for everywhere there were funerary urns and sarcophagi displaced by ploughshares but full of ash with human skulls to be seen. Statuettes and painted vases were to be found in the larger urns. Elsewhere at the necropolis at Batak, he had seen even larger urns which often contained the bones of animals. Subsequently Schliemann reported that cremation was in general use at Troy at every level he had uncovered.[34]

Long afterward John Beddoe wrote:

> When I look back upon our year in Asia Minor, it is difficult to help feeling regret that we did little, if anything, in the way of archaeological discovery during our sojourn in that surpassingly interesting country. The excavations of Schliemann at Schiblak, on the site of Ilium Novum, and as I now believe, of old Troy, have increased that regret but in truth the circumstances were not so favourable as they appeared. As Government servants, we were hardly free agents; moreover the erection of the hospital had made labour dear and almost unprocurable. Dr Goodeve in some sort of collaboration with Consul Calvert, made some sort of investigation of a site called Dardanos, a promontory stretching into the Hellespont between Renkioi and Chanak-Kalesi, and found an enormous amphora or jar containing the remains of a young child. The cranium is now in the museum of the Royal College of Surgeons, and a red-and-black tazza and small vase are in my possession.[35]

Has Renkioi a place in the story of cremation? Staff from the hospital visited the graves at Hanay Tepe and at Dardanos, where in funerary urns they found burnt human and animal bones. The *Illustrated London News* too reported the discovery of a huge amphora.[36] Their correspondent who had made excavations on the plains of Troy and on the Gallipoli peninsula recounted that, near Dardanos, some beekeepers, in search of honey, traced a bee to a hole in the ground. They were surprised, on digging, to find a jar, the interior of which was filled with honeycomb; 'when emptied, six persons entered it together and it contained them all in a sitting position.' An illustration of a pithos burial, showing a skeleton inside, accompanied the article.

Out of sight of the hospital, but not far away, the skyline of the Sigeum Ridge overlooking the Aegean Sea, was dotted with man-made eminences, bearing such names as the Tomb of Achilles and of Hector, as well as other natural hillocks. Writing 20 years later, Eassie described how he had considered that the huge tumuli, which he had frequently visited on the plains of Troy, had covered ancient funeral pyres.[37]

Frank Calvert, in 1859, appeared to put the point beyond dispute when he opened up the Hanay Tepe tumulus and found an immensity of ashes, corresponding to what might have been expected after a great burning of the dead. Calvert came to the conclusion that this was the site of the funeral pyre raised by the Trojans after the first truce.[38] Years later, after further excavations conducted with Schliemann, Calvert concluded less dramatically that the ashes were from wooden buildings and were not of human bones.[39]

Conjectures associating Renkioi and the burning of the dead can be carried further. In his *Manual of Practical Hygiene*, first published in 1864, Parkes devoted sections to the disposal of the dead.[40] He referred to the giant burial grounds which were within reach of Renkioi, and to cremation in ancient times. He realised how much space in modern cities would be saved by burial at sea or burning the body. Burials in overcrowded city churchyards had become a scandal and, with a growing population, matters would be worse in the future.

All this is evidence that the staff at Renkioi had become familiar with cremation as a method of disposal of the dead. Shallow graves favoured by the Turks on religious grounds, the smell of open graves especially notorious near the Adrianople Gate in Constantinople, and the inadequate graves on the Crimean battlefield tempered their remembrances.[41]

Parkes in his *Manual*, soon to be a standard work on public health, threw the mantle of Hygieia over cremation years before it became established in Britain. He saw cremation becoming a likely practice in the future. William Eassie became the first Secretary of the Cremation Society. Finally Spencer Wells, the senior surgeon at Renkioi and subsequently of great influence as the President of the Royal College of Surgeons, became deeply interested in cremation, and one of its most distinguished advocates. When he died at Antibes, his remains were cremated and the ashes brought back to England to be buried at the Brompton Cemetery, London. The interest of these three men in cremation, then being seriously promoted in England for the first time, may have arisen from their experiences at Renkioi. The practice of cremation led in turn to improvement in the certification of death in Britain. Is there perhaps a tenuous link between Renkioi Hospital, encircled by classical remains, and the cremation movement?

[1] The Troad is bounded on the north by the Sea of Marmara and the Dardanelles, on the west by the Aegean, to the south by the Gulf of Edremit and on the east, less precisely, by the region known in antiquity as Mysia.

[2] Rattlebrain (William Eassie). *Romaic Beauties and Trojan Humbugs*. 103. London. William Tweedie, 1858.

[3] Morley J. *The Life of William Ewart Gladstone*. 1.549. London: Macmillan, 1903.

[4] Parkes EA. *Report... Renkioi Hospital.* 36

[5] Brunton J. *John Brunton's Book with an Introduction by JH Clapham*. 68-70 Cambridge: Cambridge University Press, 1939.

[6] Rattlebrain (William Eassie). *Romaic Beauties and Trojan Humbugs*. London: William Tweedie,1858.

[7] Silver CP. *Renkioi Hospital (1855-6) and the Ancient World.* Studia Troica 2004; 14:147-156.

[8] Rattlebrain (William Eassie). *Romaic Beauties and Trojan Humbugs*. 118. London. William Tweedie, 1858.

[9] Easton DF. *Troy before Schliemann.* Studia Troica 1991. 1.111-129.

[10] Brunton J. *John Brunton's Book with an Introduction by JH Clapham.* 79 Cambridge: Cambridge University Press, 1939.

[11] Brunton J. *John Brunton's Book with an Introduction by JH Clapham.* 5 - 10 Cambridge: Cambridge University Press, 1939.

[12] I am grateful to the staff of Dundee Library and Archives Department for information about Eassie's education. It is likely that he attended the Dundee Public Seminaries (which soon after became the High School) where he would have been taught Latin and Greek by Mr Low and Mr Black.
[13] Rattlebrain (William Eassie). *Romaic Beauties and Trojan Humbugs.* 110.
[14] Eassie W. *Cremation of the Dead.* London: Smith Elder. 1875.
[15] Robinson M. Frank *Calvert and the Discovery of Troia.* Studia Troica 1995.5. 323-341.
[16] Rattlebrain (William Eassie). *Romaic Beauties and Trojan Humbugs.* 155. London: William Tweedie, 1858.
[17] Rattlebrain (William Eassie). *Romaic Beauties and Trojan Humbugs.* 153. London: William Tweedie, 1858.
[18] Numbers 213 and 211 in Frisch P. *Inschriften griechisher Studie aus Kleinasien,* Band 3 Bonn 1975.
[19] *Lancet* 1868; 2:55.
[20] *Lord Moran On Credulity. Lancet* 1954; 1:167.
[21] Beddoe J. *Memories of eighty years.* 104-109. London: Arrowsmith, 1910.
[22] Cook J M. *The Troad. An Archaeologocal and Topographical Study.* 204. Oxford: Oxford University Press, 1973.
[23] Beddoe J. *Memories of eighty years.* 110. London: Arrowsmith, 1910.
[24] Beddoe J. *Memories of eighty years.* 120. London: Arrowsmith, 1910.
[25] Beddoe J. *Memories of eighty years.* 101. London: Arrowsmith, 1910. The skull is no longer in the museum.
[26] Homer. *Iliad.* Book XXII Lines 145-152.
[27] Rattlebrain (William Eassie). *Romaic Beauties and Trojan Humbugs.* 150. London: William Tweedie, 1858.
[28] Virchow F. *Appendix 5 in Schliemann H. Ilios.* London: Murray, 1880.
[29] Newton C. *Travels and Discoveries in the Levant.* 133. London: Day, 1865.
[30] Calvert F. *Contributions to the Ancient Geography of the Troad. Archaeological Journal* 1860.17 287-296.
[31] Cook J M. *The Troad* P73-6. Oxford: Oxford University Press, 1973.
[32] Rattlebrain (William Eassie). *Romaic Beauties and Trojan Humbugs.* 114. London: William Tweedie, 1858.
[33] Rattlebrain (William Eassie). *Romaic Beauties and Trojan Humbugs.* 113. London: William Tweedie, 1858; and *Times* 28 Dec 1855.
[34] Schliemann H. *Ilios. The City and Country of the Trojans.* 720. London: Murray, 1880.
[35] Beddoe J. *Memories of eighty years.* 120. London: Arrowsmith, 1910. The skull is no longer in the museum.
[36] *Illustrated London News.* April 26 1856.
[37] Eassie W. *Cremation of the Dead.* 20. London: Smith Elder. 1875.

[38] Calvert Frank. *The tumulus of Hanai Tepe in the Troad. Archaeological Journal* 1859.16. 1-6.
[39] Calvert F. *Appendix IV in Schliemann H. Ilios.* London: Murray, 1880.
[40] Parkes EA. A *Manual of Practical Hygiene.* 457-9. London: Churchill, 1864.
[41] 'relics of the dead protrude from Sebastopol trenches' is a quotation from: Eassie W. *Cremation of the Dead.* 18. London: Smith Elder, 1875. This quotation makes it almost certain that Eassie visited the Crimea.

Chapter 10

The Closure of the Hospital

'In the Dardanelles we passed the Renkioi site bidding it farewell.' *John Brunton*

Most patients were brought by hospital ships to Renkioi, on the authority of the Inspector General, Dr Hall. Arrivals were infrequent (Table 2) because, by this stage of the war the number of sick and wounded had diminished. With the fall of Sevastopol, many hospital beds quickly became redundant. The Civil Hospital at Smyrna closed in December 1855; the last patients there transferred to Renkioi on the 20th November. The last shipload of patients arrived at Renkioi on 8 February 1856 and thereafter only a handful of patients was admitted. By July 1856 all military hospitals were closed. Brunel was already writing to Brunton, with disappointment, as early as mid-October 1855, about the expected closure of the hospital. Five months later he was reduced to suggesting that even burning it might be better than some other methods of disposal.[1] The newspapers at home soon lost interest, and after peace was declared at the end of March 1856, the homecoming of the troops was most in mind; this was complete by the early autumn of 1856.

With the war finished, there was some feeling that English influence in Turkey should continue. The war had benefited Turkish citizens financially and it was said that, as a result, peasants could now pay arrears of tax to the pashas and plant more crops.[2] Commercial opportunities were there to be grasped and there were suggestions about building a railway line from Smyrna to Istanbul, but these came to nothing. The Builder made a plea for the geological examination of the country as 'it is now opened up to us'.[3] A tourist guide, really a set of travel reminiscences rather than a guide, written late in 1855, gives a very good idea of how a traveller, after spending a season in Constantinople, viewed the British relationship to Turkey, even before the war ended. His religious views were in evidence and he had objections to the war, which he thought was in the interests of the British ruling class rather than the working class which bore its brunt. He greatly admired the fertility and beauty of Turkey, and went on to describe the pashas as desolating the country. 'The industrious poor have no refuge from extortionate tax gatherers and provincial governors. Hence the first thing by way of making this land rich and productive is to establish rulers who fear God and will do justice between man and man alike to rich and poor.' He would have magistrates and tax collectors paid a stated annual salary, abolishing a system of sale and purchase of tax. Secondly there should be a settlement of agriculturists from countries where cultivation was well conducted, so that a farmer and some few men would instruct the natives on model estates which would be settled securely by purchase, or by tenure for a long period of years; and finally public roads should be properly maintained by local authorities paid for by those whose lands benefited. 'These public roads will convey all saleable goods to market in towns and seaports, and take back, in return, western manufactured goods. Besides this, education in common and scriptural knowledge must be provided. Then the common people will be able to see all matters done and paid justly in trade and in taxes. These three things, righteous magistrates and fair taxation; agricultural skill, and roads well made; and education in reading, writing, arithmetic, geography, history, the Bible etc., will render Turkey a great and fertile paradise, as far as can be on earth... surely it is high time to diffuse the word of God in Turkey'.[4] A programme of administrative, judicial, and economic reforms (without a religious element), together with a guarantee of the rights and privileges of Christians, were terms incorporated in the peace settlement.[5]

There were suggestions that the hospital site should be regarded as British in perpetuum, but the government arranged the sale of the land. It had been hoped that the Turkish government would buy the hospital, and John Brunton visited the Grand Vizier to press this but was refused.[6] The price would have been simply that of the site and original materials without construction costs. It was left to Brunton to dispose of the hospital by auction sale. The land on which the hospital had been built was initially purchased for £407 in the name of Mrs Calvert, the wife of the British consul, necessary through a quirk of Turkish law, since Turkish land could not be bought by a foreigner. Mrs Calvert, a member of the Abbott family, was a native of Smyrna, having been born there.[7] The purchase from 49 owners had taken some time, for one refused to sell, though he would, in Turkish law, have had no right of way to reach his land, and any sale of his land would have had to be made to the British. Later the land was made over legally to the British government, the watchful War Office asking what would happen if Mrs Calvert had died meanwhile. The British government had preferred to buy land rather than accepting it as a gift from the Sultan who would have obtained it by forcible dispossession of the tenants.

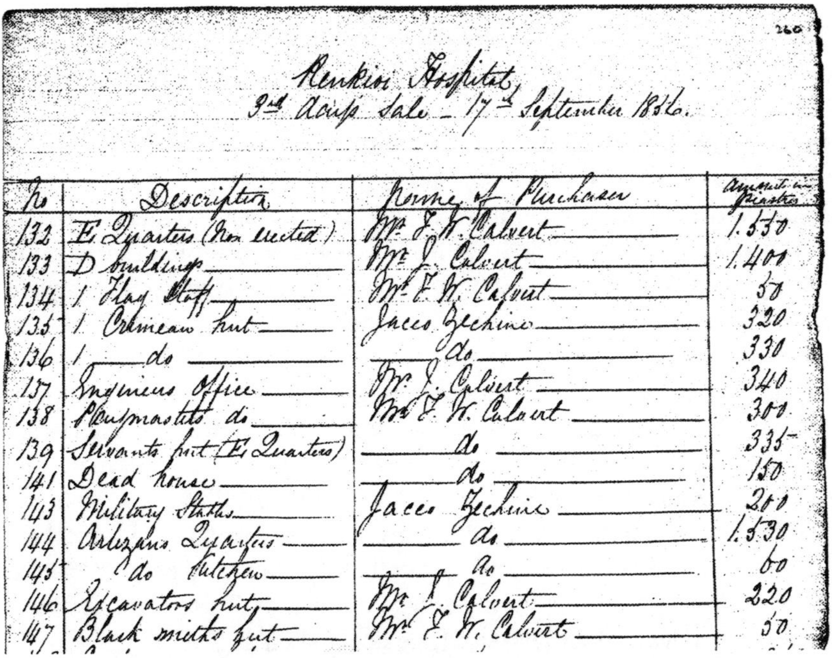

260

Renkioi Hospital,
3rd Day's Sale - 17th September 1856.

No	Description	Name of Purchaser	Amount in Piastres
132	E Quarters (Non erected)	Mr F. W. Calvert	1.550
133	D buildings	Mr J. Calvert	1.400
134	1 Flag Staff	Mr F. W. Calvert	50
135	1 Crimean hut	Jacco Zechini	320
136	1 do	do	330
137	Engineers Office	Mr J. Calvert	340
138	Paymasters do	Mr F. W. Calvert	300
139	Servants hut (E Quarters)	do	335
141	Dead house	do	150
143	Military Stables	Jacco Zechini	200
144	Artizans Quarters	do	1.530
145	do Kitchen	do	60
146	Excavators hut	Mr J. Calvert	220
147	Black smiths hut	Mr F. W. Calvert	50

Figure 18: Extract from auction record, September, 1856.
By permission of The National Archives.

The first auction to dispose of the hospital was held in July, but the highest bid for the land, with the two jetties, was for only £200 which was too low to be acceptable: Frederick Calvert had previously valued it at £1000 as he had thought that it might be bought by a shipping company, since trade with the Orient was increasing. All the items to be sold were listed, huts, partly completed huts, the stone reservoir, and iron pipes leading from it, several hundred water closets and so forth.

After this unsuccessful auction, another was held on September 16th 1856. A recent fire at Salamanca meant the hospital huts were now in demand. The hospital buildings and equipment were sold principally to Turkish buyers and members of the Calvert family in a manner described by Brunton, which rightly reflected well on him and poorly on Calvert. The machinery only attracted a bid of £400 from someone who turned out to be an agent of Calvert. This was not realistic. Brunton remonstrated with Calvert but was unable to get him to increase it. Finally Calvert said, 'Look here, Brunton, knock it down and I will give you an undertaking that you share half the profits.' Brunton was staggered at the proposition coming from the British Consul, and said, 'No Calvert, you have the wrong pig by the ear this time.'[8] Brunton then bought the lot for £1000 and sold it back later to the British government. Against orders, he now arranged its transport under the charge of his son, aged 16, to Britain in two ships on which his workforce of 150 also travelled. On arrival in England, because of the quantity of war stores being returned to the country, there were no warehouses to be found and Mr Milton at the War Office greeted him angrily. However Brunton managed to find the last two empty warehouses at the Victoria Docks in London. The ships had arrived at Spithead, and the stores were then moved from there to London without the need for any demurrage being paid. Brunton arranged their sale, netting £11,000 to £12,000. This included 500 toilets for Netley military hospital, then being built. As always he was straightforward, enterprising, energetic, and ingenious, even selling off the ward fans to provide ventilation on gunboats. The fans were delivered to the dockyard in a large wooden case marked, 'Brunton's improved machinery for ventilation'. For his work, Mr Milton, now converted, attempted to get him a payment of 5% of what had been saved by his deals, but the War Office decided on £100.[9]

After the sale of the hospital it was discovered that Mr Zecchini, the Turkish lawyer who had bought the land at the low price of 37000 piasters (about £308), was working on Mrs Calvert's behalf. In the War Office records, Calvert's statements were dismissed as 'a mere blind' and it was said, 'nor can we doubt Mr and Mrs Calvert and Senor Zecchini understand each other perfectly in the matter'. The British Government did not agree to the low price and wished to overturn the contract, suggesting £750, but the land eventually came into Calvert's possession at the price originally proposed.[10]

Brunel received payment on 26 February 1856 from the War Office of £2265. 15 shillings and 11 pence for his professional services.[11] In a generous letter dated 19th April 1856, Brunel advised Brunton on his future suggesting that he should not seek further advancement but instead emphasise past services and reward for these and then ask about future appointments.[12] In his original interview with Brunton, Brunel had perhaps been annoyed and called him a fool when he at first refused Hawes' offer of the job at Renkioi, but when the matter had been settled, proved kind and made acceptance easy, arranging for Brunton's pupil to complete his 18 months of pupillage with Brunel without charge. Brunton had nothing but respect for Brunel and never anything ill to say of him.

The medical staff of the hospital returned to Britain throughout the month of July; Dr Parkes on the Bacchante, Dr Beddoe and the medical staff on the Lady Eglinton, and Spencer Wells on the steam transport, Ossian. Beddoe wrote of his regrets at leaving, and like many others had fond memories of the people of Turkey. Brunton, on his way home to England, lunched at Constantinople with Captain Gordon (later General Gordon of Khartoum), and then took ship to Trieste, passing the enormous board he had erected which bore the words, 'Renkioi Hospital', and which was now the only sign that the hospital had ever existed. From Trieste he travelled overland.

Figure 19: Inscription, almost concealed by a fig tree, in a wall, close to its original position at the entrance to the South Pier. The mirror image letters suggest a Turkish craftsman.

Less than eighteen months after those living in Turkey had seen the hospital arrive, it existed only in their memories. Only a stone on which the name, Renkioi Hospital, is carved, now proclaims the past (Figure 19).

After closure and the sale of the site to the Calvert family, the site was returned to its original state, agricultural land. To make use of acorns and bark from Valonia oaks, a British tanning factory was established on the edge of the site and lasted until the early part of the twentieth century. At the time when the hospital was open, a Valonia oak produced an income of £2 per annum, and the best Valonia sold at £14-£15 per ton; the husks and cups were crushed to produce tannin, but not the acorns, which, if used as fuel, produce a pleasant smell. Gathering the Valonia crop resembled hop picking in Kent in the twentieth century. In the sultry nights of the autumn, the pickers could be seen sleeping outside their homes upon a heap of freshly plucked acorns, without even a mattress of straw, and covered only by a blanket. Movement, as they slept, loosened the acorns from their sheaths and saved some labour. The Turkish wives were as good harvesters as the Greek. The Turks wore ventilating gossamer veils, but the Greek 'compeeresses hide their loveliness by a heavy cotton or worsted stemella, tucked in under their chins, quite enough to ruin them in the estimation of all poetical or even poetasterical (sic) temperaments'.[13] The factory was built close to the south pier, near the site of Brunton's sleeping quarters; a low rectangle of stone, still to be found, may be a remnant.

After the war, the Calvert family ran into difficulties. Frederick Calvert, the bold entrepreneur, had overreached himself during the war in the deals he had undertaken in supplying British forces, though he was considered to have done a very good job. However Brunton's account shows that Calvert could sail close to the wind, and after the war it was thought that there were irregularities in accounts submitted for the provisioning of troops. After enquiries, his explanations were not accepted and in 1857 he was tried by the Supreme Consular Court in Constantinople and found guilty. A visit to London failed to clear his name, and in 1859 he served two months in prison. Finally, in 1860, his name was cleared but unfortunately this was not the end of his misfortunes as he became entangled in another legal case, quite unconnected with the Crimean War.

With a Turkish partner, he arranged to import and insure a cargo to be carried on the brig Possidhon. The ship then appeared to be lost but doubts emerged as to whether it had ever existed. His partner absconded, and in 1862 Calvert was accused of making a false insurance claim for goods lost. Calvert absconded, was dismissed from his posts of British consul and Prussian vice-consul, and was declared bankrupt. In 1867 he reappeared but was arrested, charged with conspiracy, and found guilty at a trial on Feb 13th, 1868.[14] He was imprisoned at Constantinople for two years. The incident excited considerable interest in England. He died in 1876. The inscription on his grave states, 'Sacred to the memory of Frederick William Calvert for 17 years Her Majesty's consul, born at Malta 11th September 1819 died at the Dardanelles 26th July 1876. The abiding love enriched by trust and reverse which stood true to him through all the vicissitudes of life clings to him in death and sanctifies his memory to many that mourn his loss'. His grave lies behind high walls in the quiet sunlit British cemetery at Çanakkale, where the Calvert family graves dominate the cemetery.

These events were a great blow to his family and to his brother Frank who too, late in life, faced punishment in connection with his brother's affairs, when he was convicted of scandalizing and vilifying the British Consul who had replaced Frederick.[15] The family continued to live in Turkey until the Second World War. A descendent, known to the local inhabitants as Coccara, is still remembered by those alive today. A final link with the Calvert family was the publication in 1911, of a letter to the *Times* from a correspondent writing from the Calvert's Thymbra Farm.[16] This described an illness among servants working there, characterised by involuntary movements, simulating dancing. Termed Tarantism, it had been known since the Middle Ages and thought of, in Turkey, as a possession, best exorcised by appeal to Saint George.

Some wrote of Renkioi in their reminiscences. John Brunton went on to be the chief resident engineer of the Scinde Railway in India, to survey the proposed line of the Indus Valley Railway and then to return to England in 1870. After this he continued with various engineering projects in slate quarries in Wales and on tramways, and died in 1899 at the age of 86.[17]

William Eassie first returned to Gloucester to work in the family firm. In his obituary,[18] his book was described as a brilliant little volume of Eastern experiences. He made no further expeditions into authorship of a similar kind. Moving to London as a consulting sanitary engineer, he advised the aristocracy and wrote a textbook about domestic sanitary arrangements, which included an allusion to Renkioi. He was a contributor to the *British Medical Journal* and *The Sanitary Record* but showed his virtuosity with papers on 'Engraving for Calico Printing'. While Secretary of the Cremation Society, of which he was a founder member, he wrote a standard work, *The Cremation of the Dead.* He died on 16 August 1888 in Hampstead.

The greatest, Brunel, was now near the end of his career. As the hazards of launching the huge steamship, the Great Eastern, began to prey on him, in the three years left to him after the closure of Renkioi, he remained active despite his failing health. Several distinguished doctors, including Richard Bright whom he had known for years, were consulted, and he was thought to have the eponymous Bright's disease, a very serious kidney disease. He would have liked to have Dr Parkes accompany him on a prolonged visit to Egypt in an effort to improve his health but this Parkes was unable to do. Brunel died on 15 September 1859, within a few weeks of the death of his great friend, Robert Stephenson. Enormous crowds gathered at their funerals.

[1] *Brunel Letter*. Book 12. P226. IKB to John Brunton 26 March 1855. Bristol University Library.
[2] Lefroy Lady. *Autobiography of General Sir John Henry Lefroy*. 156. Private Circulation. National Army Museum.
[3] *The Builder* 1856. 117.
[4] Parnauvel O T. *A trip to Turkey and Traveller's Guide to the Turkish Capital*. London. Houlston and Stoneman. 1855.
[5] Royle T Crimea. *The Great Crimean War 1854-1856*. 496. London: Little Brown and Company, 1999.
[6] Clapham JH. Ed. *John Brunton's Book* 70. Cambridge: Cambridge Univesity Press, 1939.
[7] TNA WO 43/991.
[8] Clapham JH. Ed. *John Brunton's Book* 72. Cambridge: Cambridge Univesity Press, 1939.
[9] Clapham JH. Ed. *John Brunton's Book* 80. Cambridge: Cambridge University Press, 1939.
[10] TNA WO 43/991.
[11] *Brunel letters*. DM1306 viii 28. War Dept. to Brunel signed B Hawes 26 Feb 1856.
[12] *Brunel Letter Book* 12. IKB to John Brunton 19 Apr 1856. Bristol University Library.
[13] Rattlebrain (William Eassie) *Romaic Beauties and Trojan Humbugs*. 134. London: William Tweedie, 1858.

[14] Allen SH. *Finding the Walls of Troy*. 87-92. Berkeley: University of California Press, 1999.
[15] Robinson M. *Frank Calvert and the discovery of Troia*. Studia Troica 1995; 5:323-341.
[16] *Times* 9 Sept 1911.
[17] Clapham J. Ed. *John Brunton's Book*. 159-160. Cambridge: Cambridge University Press, 1939.
[18] *Hampstead and Highgate Express* 25 August 1888 and *Gloucester Journal* 25 August 1888.

Chapter 11

Renkioi: its Place in Victorian Medical History

> 'I cannot conceal from myself that there is a strong professional feeling in the Army Medical Department which is averse to all change'.
> *Sidney Herbert to Lord Panmure, 22 November 1856*

Renkioi Hospital is now only remembered as one of the first large prefabricated building projects and the first prefabricated hospital. Largely forgotten, it was more than this. The war had brought advances in medicine, particularly military medicine and hygiene; Renkioi Hospital was evidence of these. It was a model hospital with an able staff demonstrating the best practices of the age in the setting of Brunel's inspired buildings. It exemplified new methods of hospital construction and better methods of running a hospital for soldiers, particularly hospital command by a doctor. Moreover it played a part in the formation of the Army Medical School. It looked to the future.

Though intended to be temporary and with something of the barracks in its nature, Renkioi was a modern military hospital. None of the various general hospitals serving the British Army in the East during the war, were purpose-built. The general hospitals in the Crimea, the base hospitals at Scutari and the civil hospital at Smyrna relied on old, converted buildings. Tents, or later, huts which were smaller than those at Renkioi, increased the accommodation. The Camp General Hospital, closest the front line and almost entirely concerned with treating the wounded, was tented first then hutted. Regimental hospitals and field hospitals, made up of adjoining regimental hospitals, were originally tented. As the war continued, despite their disadvantages, conditions in these hospitals, at first so bad, improved greatly. However the buildings at Renkioi outshone them all.

Again, compared with civilian hospitals, Renkioi showed advantages and marked a turning point. One hundred and fifty-four civilian hospitals and dispensaries had been founded in England, Scotland, Wales, and Ireland between 1700 and 1825[1] and, in many, the buildings had, by the Crimean War, been in use for at least fifty years. A thorough survey of civilian hospitals just after the war found that a water supply from wells, water closets at the corner of a ward, and cesspits were not uncommon, especially in provincial and rural hospitals. A new hospital at Bury St Edmunds, and a new ward at the Radcliffe Infirmary at Oxford were the only fresh undertakings recorded.[2] Conditions at the Radcliffe Infirmary, a typical provincial hospital, had been poor but times were changing for, after the war, a much improved ward was opened with a bathroom and lavatory, basins enamelled iron in a slate slab, with hot and cold water supply and waste-pipe; and the bath on wheels.[3] Renkioi provided such facilities though intended only to be a temporary hospital.

The construction of Renkioi was as much an engineering as an architectural achievement. Within a few years, prefabricated hospitals were being built during the American Civil War and again in the Franco-Prussian War of 1870. In the American Civil War, Florence Nightingale was approached by the Northern States for advice, which she gave, arranging for government information to be conveyed to Washington.[4] Prefabricated hospitals, each of 250 beds on the lines of Renkioi Hospital were constructed, and the number of hospitals rose from 16 on the Northern side at the beginning of the war to more than 350. Later much larger prefabricated hospitals were built, and the same system was then adopted for Confederate hospitals. Of these, the largest was Chamborazo Hospital at Richmond, Virginia, which accommodated 7000 patients in 150 whitewashed wooden huts. At the huge permanent Mower General Hospital in Philadelphia, and the Lincoln General Hospital in Washington, railways were in use.[5] The enormous size of these hospitals, and indeed of Renkioi, flew in the face of the opinion that smaller hospitals were safer.[6] [7]

While Renkioi Hospital was being built, Parkes had hoped that one or even two similar hospitals would be built but the need never arose. Prefabrication did not necessarily ensure success. The Turkish General hospital in the Crimea had hutted accommodation for 336 patients, with 14 patients in each of 24 huts. The huts were British, made of wood and, much smaller than at Renkioi, measured 32 feet long, 18 feet wide, and 7 feet high with, in each end wall, two glazed windows, each three feet square. There was a single door. Felt covered the roofs, but the woodwork was in a poor state, letting in the elements. Equipment in each ward included two large basins, other smaller basins, and a stove. The interior of the huts looked not unattractive. However, despite having British officers, there was unbelievable squalor. The latrines were near the huts, and the Turkish patients were filthy, infested, and relieved themselves indiscriminately outside and inside the huts.[8] An inferior British prefabricated design had been rendered entirely unacceptable by Turkish ideas of hygiene. Without Brunel and indeed Parkes, who knows what could have happened at Renkioi?

Its place assured in engineering and architectural history, the question can now be asked whether Renkioi has a particular place in medical history. Built too late in the war to make great claims, for the Victorians it was a significant advance. As a civilian hospital in military guise it was unique, a model hospital with important lessons for the army. With the war over, interest waned and its subsequent lapse into obscurity was a tacit sign that the army preferred to forget it. The concept of a civil hospital was taken by many during the war as a slur on the regular army medical services, so that there was no place subsequently for it in army annals. The official medical history of the war was a compilation of the records of the doctors engaged in the campaign.[9] This enormous and moving document; vividly describing the immense difficulties endured, recorded what had occurred but made few recommendations for the future. Civil doctors and Renkioi Hospital were scarcely mentioned.

The army did not like a civilian intrusion but the experiment of a civil element was intended to be short-lived. In July 1856, three months after the war ended, a Parliamentary Committee under the chairmanship of Mr Stafford, with army medicine well represented, agreed that the civil arrangement, however expedient in the Crimean War, should not be repeated.[10] Underused, Renkioi Hospital had existed too late in the war to prove itself. As a model hospital about which no complaints were ever made, it stood in absolute contrast to the earlier days of Scutari and to much else that had happened. Distance from the Crimea was a material disadvantage but, as transport of patients by sea improved, became less important. The Parliamentary Committee's Report can be taken as the military judgement of Renkioi, in short, no merit.

After the war, a Royal Commission was set up under the chairmanship of Sidney Herbert, to enquire into the sanitary state of the army, the organisation of military hospitals and the treatment of the sick and wounded. Its Report, published in 1858, was a wonderful exposition of army conditions, and set out the lessons of the war.[11] The evidence sometimes horrified those present. Evidence and discussion about Renkioi, covered important points. The Commission then formulated a series of recommendations, many of which, despite opposition from the War Office and the military, over the years came to be accepted.

The Commission was largely the work of Florence Nightingale, in concert with her band of advisers, and Sidney Herbert. In November 1856, she visited the Queen at Balmoral and there met Lord Panmure, the Secretary of State for War (whose ancestral home was nearby at Brechin), laying before him plans for the Commission and its possible membership, a discussion which later continued in London.[12]

Florence Nightingale's dry sense of humour often shows in her letters; her notes of the interview with Lord Panmure, called 'Pan' throughout, are delightful.[13] Florence Nightingale had a penchant for nicknames and often referred to the burly Panmure as the 'Bison'. He was from time to time afflicted by gout, 'in the hands', Sidney Herbert said, 'and this explains his not writing'. 'His gout is always handy,' she retorted.[14] Sidney Herbert was to be Chairman of the Commission, and after some juggling the members of the Commission were carefully chosen, in effect by Sydney Herbert and Florence Nightingale, though Lord Panmure gave the final approval. As the Commission closed in 1858, General Peel succeeded Lord Panmure as Secretary of State for War. About a year later, Sidney Herbert succeeded Peel and went on, until his death in 1861, to initiate the reforms proposed by the Commission.

Constitution of the Commission

Rt. Hon. Sydney Herbert - Chairman
Members
Augustus Stafford MP. Member of Roebuck Committee 1855. Visited Scutari and Renkioi.
Andrew Smith. Director General. Army Medical Department.
Thomas Alexander CB. A serving medical officer who, as Florence Nightingale's choice, followed Andrew Smith as Director General but died soon after taking office.

Sir John McNeill. Surgeon in India. Diplomat. Chairman of the board of supervision of the Scottish Poor Law Act. Chairman of the Supplies Commission. 1855. Friend and adviser of Florence Nightingale.
Sir Thomas Phillips. Large landed proprietor in Wales. Lawyer.
James Ranald Martin. Inspector General of Army Hospitals.
Sir James Clark M.D. Bt. Physician (see Chapter 3).
John Sutherland M.D. Leader of the Sanitary Commission 1855. Adviser to Florence Nightingale over many years. Visited Renkioi.
Dr Graham Balfour. Army doctor, an expert on statistics. Secretary

The first witness was examined on 13 May 1857. Many witnesses were questioned and there were written answers from Florence Nightingale who was not a member of the Commission. Her views were known to the members of the Commission, nearly all of whom she knew well, and indeed for whose appointment to the Commission she had been largely responsible. Before the Commission sat, Florence Nightingale saw every one of the witnesses herself and reported to Sidney Herbert what each, in public, could tell him as a witness.[15] It was an exhaustive and fair enquiry revealing what had gone wrong.

The Commission's enquiries about Renkioi were limited to questions for Sir John Hall and Dr Parkes. Hall thought the Civil Hospitals very expensive, that Renkioi was built too late, when upwards of 3000 empty beds were available elsewhere, and that it was too far from the Crimea. Hall never visited Renkioi and never showed it any favours. In summary he had nothing to say in support of Renkioi.[16]

Dr Parkes' evidence was particularly concerned with administrative arrangements, differing from those in a military hospital. Parkes had been sent to Renkioi with instructions that he was wholly responsible for the efficiency of the hospital; he was, of course, a civilian, though with army experience. Renkioi was unlike a military hospital where many administrative matters were the responsibility of a combatant officer. At Renkioi, Parkes held overall responsibility, and the combatant officer's responsibility was confined to military and guard duties only. Parkes' relationship with the Purveyor and Engineer, who were directly under his authority, was much more effective than in a military hospital. On his order, the Purveyor would provide the supplies required either from store or after purchase. If the Purveyor regarded Parkes' order as extremely extravagant, he could refer to the War Office, but he was to issue the stores under protest meanwhile. At Scutari, if he chose, the Purveyor had simply not issued stores, leading to endless frustration. There was another very important practical difference. It was Parkes who had selected the stores in England, and he had a complete list of these which, transported to Turkey, were there, at hand, for the Purveyor to draw on. Under conditions of active service, such an arrangement in military hospitals was impracticable. At Renkioi, until issued, stores were the Purveyor's responsibility; thereafter the responsibility for them passed to Parkes. His relationship to the Engineer was different to that in a military hospital where the engineer took his orders from the military Commandant who might or might not wish to follow the recommendation of the Principal Medical Officer. At Renkioi, he took them directly from Parkes and proceeded with the work of construction, alteration or repair. If thought too costly, the engineer still had to proceed while the opinion of the War Office or, if it were urgent, of the military Commandant at Scutari, was sought. Parkes believed that the arrangement at Renkioi was precisely what was required in a military hospital.[17] Sir John McNeill wanted a supremo as governor of the hospital, in charge of all administrative arrangements and entirely unconnected with the depot. He preferred a military man rather than a doctor. A doctor should be in charge of medical matters; directing a scavenger would be degrading for a doctor.[18] Florence Nightingale favoured 'one executive responsible head, call him governor, commandant or what you will; and let it be his sole command and whether a military, medical or civilian officer, the possession of administrative talents point out a man for the work.' A principal medical officer and his staff would also be required.[19]

Despite lengthy discussion, the Commission did not recommend a change and agreed that large base hospitals should be commanded by a Governor who should be military not medical.[20] Andrew Smith, the Director-General, dissented from the Commission's conclusions over three matters, one of which was the command of a military hospital, a subject about which he must have known more than anyone.[21] He preferred the arrangement which Parkes had described, and which had been uniquely demonstrated at Renkioi of a doctor in complete charge of the hospital.

Other matters which were touched upon included the ordering of diets. What at Scutari should have been a simple administrative arrangement, for Florence Nightingale was a frequent frustration.[22] The patient at Renkioi could see on the bed ticket what had been ordered and complain if it were not forthcoming. At Renkioi, some orderlies who had been appointed as civilians, were directly under Parkes' command but others, often with lesser education, were soldiers under the command of the military commandant. Parkes felt that it would be much more appropriate for all to be under the command of the Principal Medical Officer.

With ideas about an army medical school in the air, Parkes also gave evidence about the education of doctors. As an expert he was questioned about medical students and the methods of entry to the East India Company's medical service. If an army medical school were to be established, the army and its doctors would learn about the immense importance of hygiene. Dr Sutherland suggested that not only medical, but all officers, would benefit from instruction in hygiene, but this was a step too far for the Commission to advocate specifically.[23]

For Hall, with great responsibilities in the field, the civil hospitals seemed to present no opportunity and he felt they were foisted upon him. To enlarge upon his position, it is known that he always thoroughly disliked the idea of civil help, and his own records on the subject are interspersed with bitter comments. Dr Mayer, the Superintendent at Smyrna, with his high salary and his initial lack of a British medical degree, was a particular target. Hall remarked on the magnificent style in which the civil hospitals were equipped and the liberal rate of pay to those who were in no way superior to army medical officers yet placed in charge of comparatively small hospitals, and rewarded with salaries of £2000 a year, quarters, and table. In contrast, 'the head of their [our] own department with all his labours, cares, and responsibilities had only £1200. Even the Surgeons and Physicians of the civil establishments had a higher daily rate of pay than the Inspector-General of Hospitals in the field [himself] who had served 40 years in every quarter of the globe, and was burdened with responsibility of nearly 100 separate hospital establishments and the labour of superintending the Medical Department of the whole army in the field'.[24] Entirely understandable, these remarks certainly confirmed Smith's initial fears of the likelihood of jealousy. Both Smith and Hall had the interests of the army doctors working under them at heart. Hall thought of his own officers as 'overtasked, badly paid and uncommonly well abused', and felt throughout that civilian doctors received a scale of pay, and a civil hospital an amplitude of resources, denied the army.

Civil hospitals were acute general hospitals with large staffs. The call for the civil hospitals was made in early 1855, just as the need for beds was at its height, but by May, Hall wanted beds for convalescence and, as the first ships arrived at Renkioi, Florence Nightingale wrote to Benjamin Hawes at the War Office to say Renkioi should be restricted to 500 beds and that more were not needed.[25] With plenty of beds now available, Hall was soon saying that the large staff at Renkioi was doing nothing, and patients were only sent there because he, Hall, received instructions to send them. In November, not very long after Renkioi had begun to receive patients from the Crimea, Colonel Lefroy had arrived with the express purpose of running down the medical establishment in the East.[26]

Hall too had always had his eyes on another site, Sinope. On 14 Feb 1855, Hall wrote to Lord Raglan to suggest establishing a hospital at Sinope, and Raglan sent one of the Commissioners of the Sanitary Commission to visit, but this visit did not take place until May 30th,[27] when building at Renkioi had begun. The opinion was that the site at Sinope was very satisfactory except for the water supply which would be insufficient unless expensive engineering works were undertaken. On the information he had been given, Hall felt that, 'with good springs near, and old Roman cisterns which merely require some little repair to render them serviceable', the objection was groundless, particularly as many animals of the Commissariat and Land Transport Corps were satisfactorily kept there.[28] Despite advantages which Parkes outlined, Hall would have preferred Sinope. Hall, who had served in the hospitals after Waterloo, was looking back to the past for this was no way to deal with Brunel's demand for a good water supply.

Pique, too, may have influenced the transfer of patients to civil hospitals. Dr Pinkoffs certainly held this view of Hall's actions. The *Times* questioned why a civil hospital formed at great expense should be underused in a despatch dated 10 Oct 1855 (i.e. just as Renkioi Hospital became fully operational):

> From a correspondent:
>
> Permit me to express my wonder that the hospitals at Renkioi and Smyrna should be permitted to remain empty. It is well known that threats have been uttered that they should both 'be starved out' and the medical men should have no other

> employment than 'picking their teeth'. But the appointment of an inspector, chosen from among those who have had better taste than to countenance such expressions, and whose duty should be to apportion the cases of both the sick and wounded, would remove all difficulties and be very beneficial to the soldier. Never has the head of the army Medical Department had such material to work with. He might have established a new era in his department of the profession. How the advantages so liberally offered by Government and the British public have been turned to account I must leave to others to explain.[29]

All this was common knowledge. Dislike of the civil element probably contributed to the small number of transfers to Renkioi Hospital but the hospital opened when the pressure on beds had eased, and there must have been less incentive to transfer a patient particularly to a hospital far distant from the main base at Scutari. Had the will been there, perhaps more use of Renkioi would have been made.

At a personal level too, civilian doctors endured unpopularity when they found themselves cold-shouldered by the combatant military officers in command of hospitals, and sometimes by both regimental and hospital army doctors. For Pinkoffs, a civilian, working at Scutari, there were many frustrations, only lightened by his admiration for Florence Nightingale and her work.[30] Jealousy and animosity dwindled when Civil Surgeons and army colleagues worked side by side in the Crimea. However, not even Sir John Hall failed to recognise the worth of some Civil Surgeons, for when he cited Macleod's opinion of hospital ventilation, he recommended him with, 'we will see what the opinion of the civil surgeons employed in the general hospital was. These gentlemen are all eminent in their profession, they are men of high honour, and have no interest in the question beyond the cause of truth'.[31]

With more important matters to consider, the Royal Commission expressed no opinion about the hospital. Renkioi Hospital, which both Stafford and Sutherland, members of the Commission, had visited, was an encouraging contrast to the poor state of the permanent army hospital at Fort Pitt, Chatham, reported to the Commission.[32] During the war it received good coverage in the pages of the *Times,* while technical details appeared in medical journals and the *Builder*. Very significantly, Florence Nightingale, pivotal to the Commission, was well aware of Renkioi. Besides influential members of the Commission such as Sir James Clark, who had played a major part in commissioning the Hospital, the many witnesses, including Parkes himself, who had the ear of the medical profession, had ample opportunity to discuss Renkioi amongst themselves and spread its lessons more widely. Material reminders were the water closets which Brunton had had shipped back from Renkioi and which were installed in the new military hospital at Netley.[33] Finally and decisively, the War Office with Sidney Herbert, the Minister, and Hawes the Under Secretary, knew every detail of the hospital. So many knew about Renkioi that it is hard to believe that, despite the army's dislike of the 'civil element', all Renkioi's lessons were overlooked.

Andrew Smith, holding the most senior position in the army medical services, had recommended Renkioi's very system of command in his dissenting addendum to the Report. Soon after the Commission closed, Queen's Regulations[34] were altered. Female nurses were to be employed in General Hospitals, and General Hospitals were to be under the command of a Governor or Commandant, selected by the Secretary of State for War on account of special qualifications. Under the authority of the Officer Commanding the Forces, he should have supreme control over all matters connected with the condition and efficiency of the hospital, and full authority over any person belonging thereto. In his absence, his duties devolved to the Principal Medical Officer. A combatant officer was still to be in command, and it was only later that a change was made, and a medical officer, not a combatant officer, was put in complete command.[35] At Renkioi, as everywhere, the personality and ability of the commanding officer were paramount.

Three months before the Royal Commission had begun, Florence Nightingale had received an invitation (dated 18 February 1857), asking her to put her great knowledge of military medicine at Lord Panmure's disposal.[36] Her prime interest was to see the army's own medical services made effective, and she had no comment to make about a civil element in military matters. But she did not disregard the civil element entirely when she ensured that Renkioi's last legacy should be the subsequent career of Edmund Parkes. Her knowledge of Parkes and his work at Renkioi led her to put his name forward for the post of Professor of Hygiene at the Army Medical School established after the war.[37] In Professor Parkes, the army found the ideal first Professor of Hygiene.

In the autumn of 1856, Parkes had returned to University College Hospital. There, as a busy and exceptionally able physician,[38] he continued his research and teaching students. He would now be termed a clinical scientist. He began to explain pathology in chemical terms and continued work on albuminuria and kidney disease.

In 1860, came the invitation, which he accepted, to the chair of Hygiene at the newly opened Army Medical School. The Army Medical School was first established at Fort Pitt at Chatham, but in 1863 was moved to Netley Hospital when this hospital opened. Concerned with the health of both his wife and himself, he believed that they would be better suited by life in the country and they then lived for the rest of their lives at Sydney Cottage, Bitterne, on the outskirts of Southampton, some three miles (5 km) from Netley Hospital.

Parkes had shaped Renkioi. But Renkioi shaped Parkes. His early service in Burma and India had given him experience of army life where poor hygiene and tropical diseases were immediate hazards. With Renkioi had come the opportunity to create a new and potentially enormous hospital overseas. In contact with the army at a high level, he came to know many influential people. Of these, Florence Nightingale was, for him, far the most important. All this fitted him for what lay ahead. He had seen hygiene in action. And what a knowledge of water supplies and sanitation he must have gained! These were subjects not usually demanding much practical knowledge of doctors, but they helped him later to write his great text book of hygiene. Had he never been at Renkioi, his career might simply have continued at University College Hospital without emphasis on this new subject.

At the new school, Parkes was one of three professors. His subject, hygiene, a new branch of knowledge dealing with the maintenance of health and emphasising that prevention is better than cure, had an overall application which made it the most immediately valuable of the subjects taught. Aware of the importance of expert knowledge, Sidney Herbert in chiding Hawes, had said that, 'It was the belief that uninstructed common sense is sufficient that has destroyed our armies, and makes them costly now'.[39]

Parkes' great contribution to the school was teaching based on research. Characteristically, he gave his first lecture on an unexpected topic, 'The Cure of Old Age and the Preservation of Youth'.[40]. His theme was that good health in earlier life was the best passport to a worthwhile old age.

An extract describes his intent. 'By attention to what is taught in this school you will be prepared to enter on your service, and to perform its multifarious duties with success; ... in all the varied phases of that famous military life which you will accompany and witness, officers and men should alike turn to you with confidence as able to do for them all that can be done in their hours of sickness and peril. You will be recognised as a worthy associate in that grand English army... In endeavouring to preserve the health of others you will ensure your own; and when old age comes, it will not be as an evil to be cured, but as an ending which worthily crowns a life of labour...'

His lecture gives a good idea too of Parkes' own generous nature and his idealism and patriotism, and of the times in which he lived.

Valued widely for his educational interests, Parkes became one of the original members of the first General Medical Council and was first to bring the subject of medical education to its attention by the publication of concise, thorough, and logical suggestions for medical training, ever a controversial subject.[41]

At the Army Medical School, he undertook important investigations for the army about feeding, clothing, and the soldier's comfort. Often these were balance experiments estimating intake and output and concerned with food values, diet and exercise, and protein metabolism. In searching for concentrated foods with a high energy value, he investigated extracts of meat and was sufficiently well informed to give advice about preparing for Arctic expeditions, though he had himself never worked in a cold climate.

Parkes applied his scientific skills to immediate practical problems. A teetotaller himself, he saw the appalling depredations of alcohol, well known in ordinary society and notorious amongst soldiers. Thus, in the last months of the campaign, two of the only four deaths in the 19th Regiment (Chapter 7), were due to drunkenness. To find out more, Parkes watched the effect on a single subject, a soldier previously in the Abyssinian campaign, of giving varying quantities of alcohol of different kinds (spirits, wines of various grades, brandy) under otherwise unvarying conditions. Each investigation took about a month but, during one, the subject felt so ill, as a result of the large dose of brandy (eight ounces) which he was asked to take, that he could not complete the experiment. Parkes could summarise his findings by writing, 'with regard to the propriety of this healthy man taking any alcohol, we have no hesitation he would be better without it.'[42]

Equipment demanded scientific attention, and he became a member of General Eyre's pack committee.[43] After the war, the stock, a smart collar worn for appearance to ensure an upright posture, advocated only by die-hards and a source of great discomfort, was abolished without even the formality of scientific appraisal. Another serious discomfort arose from the heavy load carried in a pack on the back by the soldier. Weakness and numbness, which could last 24 hours, could result. The pack committee conducted extensive trials to compare four improved pack designs. One design considered was that of Parkes, who suggested metal bars to throw part of the weight on the hips. Though the metal bars did not find favour, Parkes showed a mastery of the subject and, using physiological principles, very satisfactory equipment was devised. The improved equipment allowed the soldier to carry a weight of 45 lbs.

Because of his reputation, he was asked to review various public health problems in the civilian population. Before the war he had carefully analysed the earliest cases of the London cholera epidemic of 1849 and found no evidence of patient to patient transmission by direct contact (contagion). In 1865, he was asked by John Simon, then Medical Officer of the Privy Council,[44] to investigate an outbreak of cholera on his doorstep in Southampton with cases at Bitterne. In 1871, he accepted another epidemiological task, investigating the sanitary state of Liverpool, with John Burdon-Sanderson, another great pioneer of Public Health.[45] There they realised the dire effects of poverty, and recommended better transport and wider streets as answers to health concerns, venturing beyond epidemiology and sanitary matters into social pathology and its cure. They concluded, 'we think it impossible that those great employers of labour who show such remarkable talents for organization and administration, should not be able to deal also with the problem of the foul social life which many of those who labour for them are leading.' Social medicine became an academic discipline some 70 years later.[46]

Parkes recorded progress at the School in a valuable yearly army report,[47] but his most widely known and long lasting achievement was his text book of hygiene. This, *A Manual of Practical Hygiene,*[48] like the yearly report, included reference to his own investigations. It was the record of a lifetime's observation and practice, and brought together the new subject of hygiene in a masterly way. As always his views were very clearly expressed. It first appeared in 1864, and by his death in 1876 had run to four editions. The last edition, with a widened scope and other editors, appeared in 1891 so that the book proved itself over more than thirty years. Though written primarily to meet military requirements, it also became the standard work on hygiene in civil life and was even recommended, admittedly by William Eassie, for use by every householder. It was not quite the first textbook of hygiene, for *A Treatise on Hygiene, with special reference to the Military service*[49] appeared in the United States in 1863, a product of the American Civil War, and the work of the Surgeon-General U.S. Army.

In the Manual, Parkes, using his experience at Renkioi, advised that, for the military hospital at the rear, specially erected buildings were better than using existing buildings; they should have water closets and sewers.

The book was an outstanding achievement and was the bible of a new philosophy. That philosophy was the belief that the doctor and the army medical service should be responsible, not merely for the soldier in sickness, but for preventing sickness from ever arising. Henceforth the aim of the Army Medical Services was the promotion of health and the prevention of disease.

Throughout his life, Parkes was well known for his energy and persistence, but his health was often poor. Late in life he was recommended for the post of Physician to the Queen in succession to Sir James Clark, but felt bound to decline for reasons of health. Through much of the last year of his life he was ill, suffering from tuberculosis. In his last illness, the Queen sent a letter of good wishes via his great friend and colleague, Sir William Jenner, and Florence Nightingale was permitted to send a trained nurse to look after him.[50] He died at Bitterne from generalised tuberculosis on 16 March 1876. A post-mortem examination was carried out as Parkes himself had requested.[51]

Figure 20: Stone bearing the initials E.A.P at St Alfege's Church, Solihull

His wife, who was three years older than him, died three years before him after a long period of suffering. She had been ill with valvular heart disease and congestion of the lungs for many years. No mention of tuberculosis was made, so that her death had no connection with the infectious disease from which her husband suffered. He was buried in the same grave as his wife at Solihull (her original home). The grave headstone was removed in 1962. A stone, with his initials engraved, remains in the churchyard of St Alfege's Church, Solihull (Figure 20). The initials of his wife, Mary Jane Parkes, are immediately above his.

After his death, in referring to the Army Medical School, Florence Nightingale said of Parkes that 'he was the mainspring of that watch'.[52] There were far more expressions of regard than were usual even in Victorian times, tributes to someone who had become known as the Father of Hygiene. That year (1876) he was to give the Harveian Oration, the most important of the lectures given at the Royal College of Physicians. Instead, after his death, his lecture was delivered by his friend, Sir William Jenner, then President of the Royal College of Physicians.[53] Sir William also delivered an eloquent and moving address.[54] Further afield, Baron Mundy, Professor of Military Hygiene at Vienna, said, 'All the Armies of the Continent should, at parade, lower their standards craped, if only for a moment, because the founder and best loved teacher of military hygiene of our day, the friend and benefactor of every soldier, Edmund Parkes, is no more.'[55]

On hearing of his death, Europe's most distinguished living soldier, the Prussian Field Marshal, Helmuth Von Moltke, declared that every regiment in Europe should have paraded on the day of his funeral and presented arms in honour of one of the greatest friends a soldier ever had.[56] His memory is perpetuated by the inscription of his name on the cornice of the London School of Tropical Medicine in Malet Street in London for all to read, along with those of other great pioneers.

At University College London, a Museum of Hygiene was opened in his memory in 1877, though later closed. A bust of Parkes is presently in the College library. In his memory, the army instituted a monetary prize and gold medal for the best essay on hygiene, open to serving officers, and a bronze medal for the best hygiene student in every batch of students attending the Army Medical School. His portrait was hung in the mess at Netley.[57] These were appreciations of a life in which Renkioi had played an important part.

Very soon after Parkes' death, Robert Koch announced the cycle of the anthrax bacillus and a new era of medicine began.

The story of Renkioi is of enterprise and excellence, and its underuse should not be thought of as failure. Conceived at the worst moment of the war, within weeks the hospital was being landed in Turkey and by August was ready to take 500 patients. Sufficient patients were treated to prove its worth as a model hospital. Its distance from the battlefield was a calculated disadvantage weighed against others. Only sufficient patients to justify the resources expended were lacking, This was not a planning mishap, for nobody was to know how the campaign would go and whether the second winter of the war would be worse than the first. Nothing suggests that Renkioi would not have been of immense value had the war continued and the strain on Scutari not been relieved.

Renkioi was a model hospital demonstrating good administration and good practice. The worth of female nurses looking after military patients was evident from the start. Renkioi can claim to have left two distinct legacies to the army. Hospital command by a doctor holding *full* responsibility for the hospital (as demanded of Parkes by the War Office), was proved to be effective. Later the army accepted this command structure. The other legacy was the appointment of Edmund Parkes as the first Professor of Hygiene at the new Army Medical School. Hygiene was the most important subject taught, and in Parkes the School had the ideal professor. For the Victorians, Renkioi was a signpost to the future.

[1]Gibson AG *The Radcliffe Infirmary* 4. Oxford: Oxford University Press, 1926.
[2] Bristowe JS, Holmes T. in: *6th Report of the Medical Officer to the Privy Council*, 1863. *Parliamentary Papers. Report for the Commissioners*. Vol xxviii: Appendix 15: 626, 1864.
[3] Bristowe JS, Holmes T. in: *6th Report of the Medical Officer to the Privy Council*, 1863. *Parliamentary Papers. Report for the Commissioners*. Vol xxviii: Appendix 15: 661, 1864.
[4] Woodham-Smith C. *Florence Nightingale 1820-1910*. London: Constable, 1950, 380.

[5] Thompson JD, Goldin G. *The Hospital. A Social and Architectural History*. New Haven: Yale University Press, 1975, 170-175.
[6] Snow J. *On the chief cause of the recent sickness and mortality in the Crimea. Medical Times and Gazette* 1855; 10: 457-8.
[7] Coote H. *On Hospitalism. British Medical Journal* 1869;1: 297-8.
[8] Radcliffe JN *The Turkish Hospital at Balaklava. Lancet* 1856, 1: 7.
[9] *Medical and Surgical History of the British Army which served in Turkey and the Crimea in the War against Russia* 1854-55-56. HM Stationary Office, 1858.
[10] *Parliament Papers 1856 XIII Proceedings of the Select Committee of the Medical Department (Army). Resolution* 13.
[11] *Royal Commission...Sick and Wounded 1858*. London. Stationary Office. 1858.
[12] Cook ET. *The Life of Florence Nightingale*. London: Macmillan, 1913, 1.322.
[13] Cook ET. *The Life of Florence Nightingale*. London: Macmillan, 1913, 1.330.
[14] Cook ET. *The Life of Florence Nightingale*. London: Macmillan, 1913. 1 335.
[15] Woodham - Smith C. *Florence Nightingale*. London: Constable, 1950, 288.
[16] *Royal Commission... 1858* Questions 5404-5425 Hall loathed the idea of civilian doctors doing the army's work but his comments were not unreasonable.
[17] *Royal Commission... 1858* Question 873.
[18] *Royal Commission... 1858* Question 9917.
[19] *Royal Commission... 1858* Question 10015.
[20] A century later Sir Neil Cantlie, previously Director General of the Army Medical Services, emphasised the wrongness of this decision. *History of the Army Medical Department* 2.205 Edinburgh: Livingstone Churchill, 1974.
[21] *Royal Commission... 1858*. Report LXXXIV.
[22] Goldie SM (Ed). *Letters from the Crimea*. Manchester; Mandolin, 1997, 273.
[23] *Royal Commission...Sick and Wounded 1858*. Question 9981 That the commanding officer ignored health only at his peril was not completely accepted until the Second World War. Field Marshall Slim in command of the 14th army in Burma said that good doctors are no use without good discipline. 'More than half the battle against disease is fought not by doctors but by regimental officers. It is they who see that the daily dose of mepacrine is taken....if mepacrine is not taken, I sacked the commander. I had only to sack three; by then the rest had got my meaning'. Harrison M. *Medicine and Victory. British Military Medicine in the Second World War*, 194. Oxford: Oxford University Press, 2004.
[24] Hall J. *Papers of Sir John Hall*. Observations on difficulties experienced by the Medical Department during the late war in Turkey, and the Crimean the years 1854-5 & 6 by Sir John Hall K.C.B, Inspector General of Hospitals and Principal Medical Officer to the Army. RAMC 397, Wellcome Institute for the History of Medicine.
[25] Florence Nightingale. *Letters from the Crimea*. 1854-1856 Ed. Sue M Goldie. 115. Manchester: Mandolin, 1997.

[26] Lefroy Lady (Ed.). *Autobiography of General Sir John Henry Lefroy*. 136. Private Circulation. It was on this visit that Lefroy saw a huge Turkish gun (firing stone cannon balls and dated 1454) at the 'Asiatic Fort' at Dardanelles and asked for it to be transported to England (157-159). It is now at Fort Nelson, Portsmouth.
[27] *Report to the Right Hon. Lord Panmure. Proceedings of the Sanitary Commission* 1855-56. 143. London: Harrison 1857.
[28] Wellcome Contemporary Medical Archives Centre. *Papers of Sir John Hall.* RAMC 397 FRT1-3.
[29] *Times* 10 Oct 1855.
[30] Pinkoffs P. *Experiences of a Civilian in Eastern Military Hospitals.* 79 London: Williams and Norgate, 1857.
[31] Hall J. *Sir John Hall's Rejoinder to Dr Sutherland's Reply to his observations on The Report of the Sanitary Commissioners at the Seat of War in the East in 1855 and 1856*; 17. London. Clowes, 1858 RAMC 397 Wellcome Institute for the History of Medicine. Macleod dedicated his own *Notes on the Surgery of War in the Crimea* to Hall.
[32] *Royal Commission... 1858* Appendix XLIII. 465.
[33] Clapham J. (Ed). *John Brunton's Book.* 76. Cambridge: Cambridge University Press, 1939.
[34] *Regulations for the duties of Inspector-General of Hospitals and Deputy Inspector-General of Hospitals... sanitary and medical statistics and reports.* London: H.M. Stationery Office, 1859.
[35] Cantlie N. *A History of the Army Medical Department* 2.205. Edinburgh: Livingstone Churchill, 1974.
[36] Her advice, completed when she had the Report of the Commission at hand, was subsequently published privately as: Nightingale F. *Notes on matters affecting the health, efficiency and hospital administration of the British Army.* London: Harrison, 1858.
[37] Neal JB. *The history of the Royal Army Medical College.* J. Royal Army Medical Corps 1957, 103: 163-172.
[38] Parkes was a trusted physician with an enormous experience. It was he who looked after Dr (later Sir) William Jenner in attacks of typhus and typhoid (*Jenner's Lectures and Essays on Fevers and Diphtheria.* 1893). One of his more bizarre cases, ultimately fatal, was that of a sword swallower. (Wound of the oesophagus with perforation of the pericardium. Transactions of the Pathological Society 1848-50. 2.40).
[39] Stanmore Lord. *Sidney Herbert. Lord Herbert of Lea.* 2.158. London: John Murray, 1906.
[40] Parkes EA. *Introductory Lecture. Lancet* 1862; 2:381-4.
[41] Parkes EA. *A scheme of medical tuition. Lancet.* 1868; 1:441-3.
[42] Parkes EA. *Experiments on the effect of alcohol (Ethyl Alcohol) on the human body. Proceedings of the Royal Society* 1870; 18:362-393.

[43] Renbourne ET. *The knapsack and the pack. Ministry of Supply. Directorate of physiological and biological research. Clothing and Equipment Physiological Research Establishment.* No date.
[44] *8th Report of the Medial Officer of the Privy Council.* Appendix 14, 1865. HM Stationery Office, 1866. Parkes' meticulous investigation, with great attention to initial cases, showed that patients with Asiatic cholera arriving on ships from the East had brought the infection to Southampton. Some cholera patients lived at Bitterne as did Parkes himself.
[45] *Reports of Dr Parkes and Dr Sanderson on the Sanitary Condition of Liverpool.* Liverpool: Benson and Holme, 1871.
[46] Ryle JA. *Changing Disciplines: Lectures on the History, Method, and Motives of Social Pathology.* Introduction Porter D. New Brunswick. N.J.:Transaction Publishers, 1994.
[47] *Army Medical Department. Statistical, Sanitary and Medical Reports* 1859-
[48] Parkes EA. *A Manual of Practical Hygiene.* London. Churchill. 1864.
[49] Hammond WA. *A treatise on Hygiene with special reference to the Military Service.* Philadelphia. 1863.
[50] Cook ET. *The Life of Florence Nightingale* 2.318. London: Macmillan, 1913.
[51] *Lancet* 1876; 1:481.
[52] Letter to Dr Acland 17 .3.1876 quoted by Zachary Cope. *Florence Nightingale and the Doctors.* London: Museum Press, 1958.
[53] *Harveian oration.* Royal College of Physicians. 26 June 1876. Lancet 1876; 2:1-4.
[54] Jenner W. *Observations on the work and character of the late E.A. Parkes M.D., F.R.S. British Medical Journal* 1876; 2:34.
[55] Crowdy JP. (quoting Mundy J.) *Journal of the Royal Army Medical Corps* 1976; 173-174.
[56] Scott HH. *A History of Tropical Medicine* 1: 52 London: Arnold, 1939.
[57] Now at the Army Medical Services Headquarters Officers Mess at Camberley.

Appendix 1

Chronology: the Crimean War and Renkioi Hospital

5 April 1854 Declaration of War between Britain and Russia

April 1854 Landings of first British Troops at Gallipoli (now Gelibolu) and Scutari (now Uskedar). The General Hospital at Scutari opened in May 1854, and the Barrack Hospital in September.

18 May 1854 Conference at Varna. Omar Pasha, Lord Raglan, and Saint-Arnaudt, the Turkish, British, and French Commanders-in-Chief agreed to start moving troops to Varna. Landings at Varna took place in June and an allied base was established there as the jumping off point for the invasion of the Crimea.

14 September 1854 Landing on the Crimea at Calamita Bay with the object of capturing Sebastopol.

20 September 1854 Battle of Alma

25 October 1854 Battle of Balaklava and the Charge of the Light Brigade

4 November 1854 Arrival of Florence Nightingale at Scutari

5 November 1854 Battle of Inkerman

Winter 1854-1855
The siege of Sevastopol began and in November, a great gale with loss of life and enormous loss of stores emphasised the start of winter, a bitter winter continuing until the end of March 1855.

22 January 1855 Call for Civil Surgeons

8 February 1856 Smyrna Military Hospital became Civil Hospital - February 16th. Brunel agreed to undertake construction of a prefabricated hospital.

March 1855. The watershed of the war. Arrival of the Sanitary Commission at Scutari on March 4th. By April the weather was good and the siege continued

17 May 1855 First cargoes of hospital parts arrived at Dardanelles

8 September 1855 Fall of Sevastopol

2 October 1855 First shipload of war casualties received at Renkioi

1856 Negotiations for peace began in the New Year

February 1856 Last shipload of casualties received at Renkioi

30 March 1856 Treaty of Paris

June 1856 Last patients left Renkioi Hospital

July 1856 Most of Renkioi staff left for home

September 1856 Hospital sold at auction and remaining staff left

Appendix 2

Holders of the Great Offices of State (referred to in the text)

Lord Aberdeen's Cabinet (originally formed December 1852)

Prime minister and First Lord of the Treasury: Earl of Aberdeen

Chancellor of the Exchequer: W.E. Gladstone. Whole cabinet resigned 29 Jan 1855

Foreign Secretary (from February 1853): Earl of Clarendon

Secretary for War and the Colonies: Duke of Newcastle (for War only from June 1854). Resigned 1 Feb 1855.

Secretary for the Colonies (from June 1854): Sir G. Grey

Secretary at War: Sidney Herbert (Herbert remained in office but post abolished at end of 1854)

Lord Palmerston's Cabinet (formed February 1855)

Prime Minister and First Lord of the Treasury: Viscount Palmerston

Chancellor of the Exchequer: W.E. Gladstone

Foreign Secretary: Earl of Clarendon

Secretary for War: Lord Panmure

Secretary for the Colonies: Sydney Herbert

W.E. Gladstone and Sidney Herbert resigned 23 February 1855

Lord Derby's Cabinet (formed February 1858)

Secretary for War: General Peel

Lord Palmerston's second Cabinet (formed June 1859)

Secretary for War: Sidney Herbert: Created Lord Herbert of Lea, 1860. Resigned, July 1861.

Appendix 3

Medical and Other Staff – Renkioi Hospital

Doctors initially trained in England

Parkes, Edmund Alexander. Superintendent
Wells, Thomas Spencer. Surgeon
Coote, Holmes. Surgeon

Armitage, Thomas
Bader, Carl
Dix, John
Fawcas, James
Maunder, Charles
Playne, Alfred
Roberts, Bransby
Stretton, Samuel
Veale, Thomas

John Humphrey. Apothecary. MRCS LSA 1849

Doctors initially trained in Scotland

Goodeve, Henry. Physician
Robertson, William. Physician

Beddoe, John
Buchanan, George
Christison, David
Cowan, John

Dixon, Thomas
Hale, Robert
Holland, Thomas
Kirk, John
McLaren, James
Reid, Wilfred
Scott, George

The names of the above appear in TNA WO 43/991. Additional information is to be found in John Shepherd's *Crimean Doctors*. As well as those named above, he named as staff members, John Francis LSA,1834, MRCS 1835, a London trained doctor whose name does not appear in the TNA list and whose entries in the Medical Directory made no allusion to Renkioi, and two Assistant Surgeons, Field and John Fox, and two Assistant Physicians, Hooper and Parry. He hazarded that they were unqualified and appointed as dressers. Parry resigned before embarkation (TNA WO 43/991).

Ward Staff (whose names can be found in TNA WO 43/991)

There were 28 nurses filling the following posts: Lady Superintendent, Sub Matron, Head Nurse, Lady Nurse, Upper Nurses (8), Nurse (4), Under Nurse (11), Nurse & servant (1) Nurse and seamstress (1).

Thirty-three orderlies were entirely engaged in nursing, and nine others combined this with other duties, e.g. orderly dispenser.

Appendix 4

Infectious Diseases: The Causal Organisms

Discoveries made long after the Crimean War explained much that had been incomprehensible during the war. Flies, referred to and good evidence of deplorable hygiene, must have commonly conveyed infection by contaminating food.

Malaria. Parasitic. Plasmodium malariae (4 species). When an uninfected patient is bitten by an already infected female anopheles mosquito, malarial parasites pass from the salivary glands of the mosquito into the blood of the patient. The cycle of infection is continued when the now infected patient is bitten again and another mosquito becomes infected. Laveran identified the malarial parasite in the red blood cell at Constantine in Algeria in 1880. Sir Patrick Manson proposed the extra-corporeal cycle in 1894, and Sir Ronald Ross demonstrated the parasite in the Anopheles mosquito in 1897.

Typhoid. Bacterial. Salmonella typhi was first isolated in 1884. Infection by mouth, from water supplies and food contaminated by infected human excreta.

Typhus. (Epidemic). Bacterial. Rickettsia prowazekii, intracellular organisms in specific arthropods, including the louse, man becoming an accidental host. The cycle of infection is from infected louse to patient. Irritation leads to the louse faeces being scratched into the skin of the victim. The louse was demonstrated as the carrier in 1911 and the organism was identified in 1916.

Relapsing fever. Relapsing fever was due a number of different diseases. The disease still known as Relapsing Fever is characterised by gradual improvement halted suddenly by a rapid recurrence of fever, the process often later repeated. The disease in the Crimea is likely to have been louse borne, due to Burrelia recurrentis, isolated in 1873. However, accurate diagnosis was impossible. Apparently similar illnesses probably included Malta fever, a bacterial (Brucella melitensis) infection of animals, transmitted to man by drinking infected goats' milk.

Dysentery. Bacterial. Shigella of various types, invading the wall of the bowel Infection by mouth from water supplies or food contaminated by infected human excreta. The first shigella bacillus was identified in 1897.

Amoebic. Protozoan parasite, Entamoeba histolytica, living harmlessly in the lumen of the bowel but capable of invading it, causing bloody diarrhoea and, on reaching the liver, liver abscesses. Infection is by mouth from food and water supplies contaminated by a cystic form of the organism which has been passed out in human excreta. This amoeba was isolated in 1875 and later proved to be the causative organism by Robert Koch.

Cholera. Bacterial. Caused by the enterotoxin of vibrio cholerae colonising the small intestine. Infection by mouth, from human excreta contaminating water supplies and food. Robert Koch identified the bacillus in 1893.

Tuberculosis. Bacterial. Tuberculosis of the lungs, the most common form of tuberculosis, is due to Mycobacterium tuberculosis. Airborne droplets, passed from person to person commonly by coughing, spread infection. The bacillus was discovered by Robert Koch in 1882. Infection can also result from drinking milk from cows infected with tuberculosis; the bovine form of the bacillus was discovered in 1890.

Appendix 5

Admissions (A) and Deaths (D) (all causes) Renkioi Hospital October 1855 - June 1856

	Oct-Dec55		Jan-Mar56		Apr-Jun56		Oct55-Jun56	
Disease	A	D	A	D	A	D	A	D
Febris intermittens	25	0	13	9	0	0	38	9
Febris continua	122	2	120	11	0	0	242	13
Pleuritis	5	0	7	0	0	0	12	0
Pneumonia	3	0	15	0	1	0	19	0
Haemoptysis	0	0	4	1	0	0	4	1
Phthisis pulmonis	13	0	19	8	0	1	32	9
Catarrhus chronicus	9	0	16	0	1	0	26	0
Bronchitis	27	0	70	0	2	0	99	0
Asthma	1	0	10	0	0	0	11	0
Morbus cordis	15	0	11	0	0	0	26	0
Varix	4	0	1	0	0	0	5	0
Hepatitis chronica	5	0	4	0	1	0	10	0
Icterus	9	0	0	0	0	0	9	0
Peritonitis	1	1	0	0	0	0	1	1
Dysenteria Chronica	139	7	30	3	0	0	169	10
Diarrhoea	69	0	35	3	1	0	105	3
Haemorrhois	0	0	3	0	0	0	3	0
Hernia	4	0	4	0	0	0	8	0
Dyspepsia	5	0	7	0	1	0	13	0
Mania	1	0	3	0	1	0	5	0
Delirium Tremens	0	0	0	0	1	0	1	0
Paralysis	1	0	0	0	0	0	1	0
Epilepsy	2	1	4	0	1	0	7	1
Category omitted	1	0	0	0	0	0	1	0

Continued	Oct-Dec55		Jan-Mar56		Apr-Jun56		Oct55-Jun56	
Disease	A	D	A	D	A	D	A	D
Synovitis	1	0	0	0	0	0	1	0
Phlegmon et abscissus	19	0	13	0	1	0	33	0
Ulcus	4	0	6	0	0	0	10	0
Fistula in ano	2	0	1	0	1	0	4	0
Syphilitica primitiva	0	0	4	0	0	0	4	0
Syphilitica consecutiva	13	0	6	0	1	0	20	0
Bubo	3	0	0	0	0	0	3	0
Gonorrhoea	2	0	6	0	0	0	8	0
Orchitis	2	0	2	0	0	0	4	0
Morbus renum	0	0	3	0	0	0	3	0
Vulnus sclopitorum	61	1	2	0	0	0	63	1
Contusio	14	0	11	0	1	0	26	0
Fractura	1	0	4	0	0	0	5	0
Gelatio	1	0	34	2	0	0	35	2
Scorbutus	2	0	3	0	0	0	5	0
Morbi oculorum	16	0	12	0	1	0	29	0
Morbi cutis	2	0	2	0	0	0	4	0
Cyananche	3	0	4	0	0	0	7	0
Scrofula	0	0	2	0	0	0	2	0
Dropsy	0	0	2	0	0	0	2	0
Cephalalgia & vertigo	3	0	5	0	2	0	10	0
Morbi varii	13	0	14	0	3	0	30	0
Total	729	12	582	37	19	1	1330*	50

Medical and Surgical History... Russia. 2. General Hospital Returns. Table IX. 1858

*This figure is less by one than the figure in Parkes' own Report

The table shows the diagnoses of patients at Renkioi. Surgical patients were less numerous than medical and accounted for rather less than a quarter of the total. The meaning of most of the diagnostic terms in the table, though shrouded in Latin, is obvious or can be guessed. The meanings of the remainder (some completely obsolete) are listed in parentheses, as follows: Febris (fever), Haemoptysis (coughing up blood), Phythisis (lung tuberculosis), Icterus (jaundice), Haemorrhois (haemorrhoids or piles), Phlegmon (inflammation), Orchitis (inflammation of the testicle), Morbus renum (disease of the kidneys), Vulnus Sclopitorum (wound, sclopitorum probably best translated as gunshot!), Gelatio (frostbite), Scorbutus (scurvy), Cyananche (cyanosis, deep purple colouration of the skin and tissues), Scrofula (tuberculous lymphatic glands, once called the king's evil) and Dropsy (abnormal collection of watery fluid in any part of the body, particularly occurring in heart or kidney disease).[1]

[1]One diagnosis not on this list is catacausis (spontaneous combustion); not surprisingly, as not a single death from this then accepted official cause had been reported in the country.

Figure 21: Basin from a decorative fountain found near the site of the cemetery in 1999

Appendix 6

Renkioi for the Visitor

William Eassie foresaw a railway across the Troad taking the traveller anywhere. This never came about and railways are only a small part of Turkey's present transport system. The tourist from abroad can readily fly to Istanbul and then visit the countryside where Renkioi Hospital once stood. A car is much the easiest way of visiting isolated spots. Istanbul is about 5 hours from Çanakkale, by coach. Bus and coach services radiate from Çanakkale, and there is a satisfactory bus service from there to the village of Güzelyali and the shelf of land, extending seawards from the mosque, on which the Hospital stood (Figures 2a, 2b, and 2c). The distance from Çanakkale is about five miles (8 km), and a taxi is an easily available alternative.

The village of Güzelyali looks across the Dardanelles. Everywhere the view is beautiful, and particularly so in the late afternoon, when the waters of the Dardanelles, meeting the Aegean, turn to gold. The Hospital site can be easily identified as the shelf of land between the mosque and the sea; a small Turkish Naval encampment stands on its seaward margin and the Iris Hotel on its western edge. A stone bearing the name of the Hospital can be found at the southern extremity of the village concealed under a fig tree in the wall of the Girls' Sports Centre, next to the Tusan Motel (Figure 19). It stood at the landward end of the south pier. The cemetery and the hospital reservoir were situated on rising ground immediately behind the nearby mosque. Their locations can only be surmised unless some excavation is undertaken.

An ornamental basin was removed from the neighbourhood of the cemetery some years ago and is now in the garden of the Iris Hotel (Figure 21). A guide is needed to find the springs, high in the hills, supplying water to the hospital. The likely course of the underground pipe is not difficult to imagine (Figure 22).

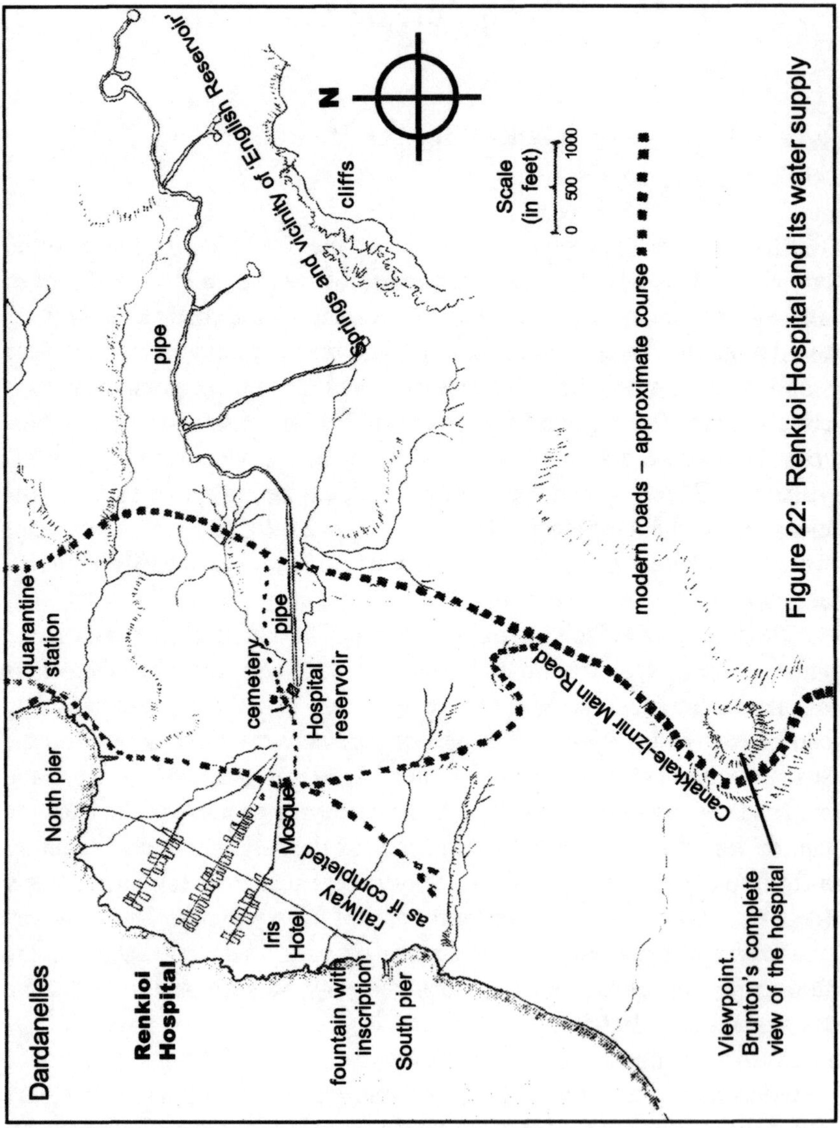

Figure 22: Renkioi Hospital and its water supply

This map appeared in *The War Correspondent*, (October 2002), Journal of Crimean War Society.

Çanakkale is the tourist centre of the district. An old fort from the days of the Ottoman Empire is now a museum largely devoted to the Great War. The disastrous Allied naval action in the Dardanelles, on 18 March 1915, which failed to force the Narrows, took place close to Güzelyali. There is also an excellent modern, archaeological museum displaying many finds, including some presented by the Calvert family. The British Cemetery with the Calvert family graves is in the centre of Çanakkale and can be visited using a key obtained from the British War Graves Commission at Çanakkale. Other British graves from the nineteenth century are to be found there including that of Lieutenant-Colonel Ferguson who died on the French steam packet Le Carie in August 1854.

The site of ancient Troy is visited by thousands of tourists every year and is less than ten miles from Güzelyali. Everywhere is evidence of the Ancient World, ranging from the tomb of Hector, seen upstanding on the skyline, to fragments of Roman tiles scattered in the woods. Close to Güzelyali and fairly easy to find are the Kemer aqueduct (Figure 15), Alexandria Troas and the columns of Yedi Tash. The Gallipoli peninsula with its poignant memories of the Great War, on the opposite shore of the Dardanelles, is the other great tourist attraction.

In Istanbul, landmarks familiar during the Crimean War include the ancient city, Stamboul, with Santa Sophia, the Blue Mosque, and the Seraglio, the erstwhile palace of the Sultans. Pera still has its grand buildings, once occupied by Lord Stratford de Redcliffe as British Ambassador, and his various counterparts, flaunting the power and wealth of their respective countries. Lord Stratford's garrison church still stands, while the enormous Galata Tower dominates the commercial quarter of Galata as it has for centuries. Further along the shores of the Bosphorus is Therapia (now Tapabya), still enticing, and once the site of the naval hospital. Views of the hills in and beyond the city, reminded many in 1854 of Highgate Hill in London, and are little changed.

Across the Bosphorus at Üskedar, the huge building with its corner turrets, once the giant Selimye Barrack Hospital, is still to be seen from the Seraglio Point. Florence Nightingale's quarters there, in what is now again a Turkish army barracks, can be visited by arrangement.

Using common sense about military matters, the Dardanelles, though of immense strategic importance, can be visited without hindrance. Laws are strictly enforced to prevent the removal of historic material from Turkey.

A photograph of the original map of Renkioi, illustrating Parkes' Report and prepared by John Brunton, is valuable to any visitor. The Wellcome Institute Library provided the copy used in this book. Published by the Nightingale Museum, London, a booklet, *Lessons from Renkioi*, is informative and has a useful map. The Crimean War Research Society web site (http://www.crimeanwar.org/) displays useful information about the Crimean War.

Index

- E -

- F -

- G -

- H -

- S -

- T -

- U -

- V -

- W -